SPOTLIGHT ON SUFFIXES

Book Two

Suffix Recognition and Use
Spelling Rules
Grammar and Vocabulary

SPOTLIGHT on SUFFIXES

Book Two
Suffix Recognition and Use
Spelling Rules
Grammar and Vocabulary

First edition published by
The Robinswood Press 2000

Design and illustrations by
Stephen Emms, Phil Goundrey and Sue Kruse.
Print by e.plan Birmingham and Antony Rowe Ltd.

The Robinswood Press

Stourbridge   England

ISBN 1-869981-618

CONTENTS

Page

ABOUT THE AUTHOR 5

INTRODUCTION 6

TEACHING NOTES AND GUIDELINES 8

SECTION 1 SUFFIXING RULES

Worksheet	Suffix		Page
1	s ing ed	Introduction and revision..	15
2	s ing ed	Revision, with -ful, -less, -ness, -ly, -y, -er, -ish............	17
3		Nouns, Verbs and Adjectives	18
4		The Double Rule..	19
5		Double Rule v̆c / v	20
6		Double Rule in longer words: Words ending in 'l'	22
7		Double Rule in longer words: Words ending in 'r'	23
8		Double Rule in longer words: Words ending in 't'	25
9a		Doubling in longer words: General Rule	27
9b		Doubling in longer words: General Rule	28
10		Drop 'e' Rule	29
11		Drop 'e' Rule	30
12		Drop 'e' Rule: Soft 'c' and 'g' words	31
13a		Nouns ending in 'y': Plural forms	32
13b		Nouns ending in 'y': Plural forms	33
14		Adding suffixes to words ending in 'y'	34
15		Adding 2 suffixes to base words	35
16		Rule Practice Sheet	36
17		Rule Practice Sheet	37
18		Rule Practice Sheet	38
19		Rule Practice Sheet	39
20		Rule Practice Sheet	40
21		Rule Practice Sheet	41
22		Rule Practice Sheet	42

SECTION 2 a) NOUN SUFFIXES

23	ness	....	43
24	tion	....	44
25	tion	....	45
26	tion	....	46
27	sion	....	47
28	sion	Related NOUNS and VERBS.................................	48
29	ity	Related NOUNS and ADJECTIVES	49
30	ity	....	50
31	ment	....	51
32	ment	....	52
33	ence	....	53
34	ance	....	54
35	cy	....	55
36	ism	....	56
37	age	....	57
38	ure tude	....	58
39	hood ship dom	....	59
40	er	....	60

41	or		....	61
42	ist		....	62
43	an		....	63
44	ess ling ee		....	64
45		Noun Revision Sheet: Abstract Nouns	....	65
46		Noun Practice Sheet	....	66
47		Noun Practice Sheet	....	67

SECTION 2   b) VERB SUFFIXES

48	s ing ed	Verb suffixes for tense	....	68
49	en		....	69
50	ate		....	70
51	ate		....	71
52	ify		....	72
53	ise		....	73
54	ise		....	74
55		Verb Practice Sheet	....	75

SECTION 2   c) ADJECTIVE SUFFIXES

56a	ing ed	as Adjective endings	....	76
56b	ing ed	as Adjectives of Feeling	....	77
57	y		....	78
58	ful ness		....	79
59	worthy	also -some, -like, -ish	....	80
60	ous		....	81
61	ous		....	82
62	tious cious		....	83
63	al		....	84
64	al		....	85
65	tial cial		....	86
66	able		....	87
67	ible		....	88
68	ent		....	89
69	ant		....	90
70	ic		....	91
71	ive		....	92
72	ive		....	93
73	ate		....	94
74	ary		....	95
75	ory		....	96
76		Adjective Practice Sheet	....	97
77		Adjective Practice Sheet	....	98
78		Adjective Practice Sheet	....	99

SECTION 2   d) ADVERB SUFFIX 'ly' AND WORD FORMATION PRACTICE SHEETS

79	ly	as VERB Modifier	....	100
80	ly	as ADJECTIVE Modifier	....	101
81		Word Formation: Practice Sheet 1	....	102
82		Word Formation: Practice Sheet 2	....	103
83		Word Formation: Practice Sheet 3	....	104
84		Word Formation: Practice Sheet 4	....	105
85		Word Formation: Practice Sheet 5	....	106

SUMMARY OF SUFFIXING RULES 107

ANSWERS 108

ABOUT THE AUTHOR

Gillian Aitken MA, PGCE, RSA Dip. TEFL, AMBDA, Dip. Psych. (Open)

Gillian Aitken trained originally as an English teacher and taught in schools for a number of years. More recently she has concentrated on areas in teaching English where a specialised approach is required. These have included teaching English to pupils with Special Needs, teaching pupils where English is a Second or a Foreign Language, and adult literacy work with the Dyslexia Institute.

Ms Aitken therefore has a unique range of experience gained practically both in Britain and abroad, and through further academic study. This background has provided her with both a clear understanding of the challenges faced by teachers in a variety of different situations and also perfect opportunities to develop a variety of exercises – such as the word-search exercises in her first publication, *Spotlight on Words,* the consonant blend exercises of *Spotlight on Blends* Books One and Two, and now the Suffix exercises in *Spotlight on Suffixes* Books One and Two. All these exercises meet the educationalist's requirement to build spelling and reading skills whilst the pupil becomes engrossed in the challenge and enjoyment of the exercises themselves.

Ms Aitken lives in Sussex and continues to work as a specialist English teacher. She is an Associate Member of the British Dyslexia Association and a Graduate Member of the British Psychological Society.

INTRODUCTION

'Spotlight on Suffixes', Book Two, builds on the basic introduction to suffixes and suffixing rules covered in Book One. The English language relies heavily on suffixing to convey grammatical meaning and structured teaching about the form and function of suffixes in English is a useful way into grammar, helping pupils to recognise parts of speech and manipulate word forms. Whereas Book One covered only the most common suffixes in English, which derive from Old English, the material in this book provides comprehensive coverage of the very wide range of noun, verb and adjective suffixes which have entered English mostly from French, Latin and Greek. By doing the various worksheets, pupils will thus be learning not only about word structure and grammar, but gaining knowledge about word derivations and extending their vocabulary.

The book is divided into two main sections. The first one deals with the basic suffixing rules, consolidating and extending the material in Book One. The first few worksheets deal with suffix recognition and introduce pupils to the concept of suffixes as grammatical markers. The major suffixing rules are explained and practice sheets given. There is a detailed section on doubling in longer words which was not covered in Book One. The rule practice sheets at the end of Section One follow the same format as those in Book One, but use a wider range of suffixes and are at a higher level of difficulty. A summary of suffixing rules in English is given in Appendix A at the back of the book.

Section Two deals with specific suffixes and is sub-divided into three main parts dealing with noun, verb and adjective suffixes. For suffixes which are of high frequency such as 'tion', 'ate' and 'ous', there are worksheets at two levels of difficulty. This allows for differentiated work within the classroom, providing a challenge for more pupils with a higher vocabulary. The various suffixes are introduced and practised individually, but then brought together with other suffixes for contrastive purposes in the practice sheets at the end of each sub-section. There is a short final section which consists of five practice sheets in word formation which involves manipulating parts of speech. Answers to all the exercises are given at the back of the book.

The worksheets vary in format, but aim to be clear in layout and presentation so that they can be used independently of the teacher if necessary. Many of the worksheets would be suitable for homework in this respect. Each suffix is introduced in a box at the top of the worksheet with some brief information about derivation, function and meaning. Instructions are always underlined and follow a similar format. As in Book One, efforts have been made to present new vocabulary in a meaningful context. There are many word-completion exercises in Book Two which can take the form of anagrams, word quizzes or gapped words with letters missing. Whilst some of these are relatively difficult as they stand, teachers can easily make the completion task easier by providing more letters, or giving the first two or three letters for anagrams. There is thus plenty of scope for varying the material to suit the needs of individual pupils. Several word-searches have been included to provide an element of fun. Exercises in word meanings and word-formation are interspersed with exercises on adding suffixes to base words, so that there is constant recycling of the basic suffixing rules. In some worksheets, pupils are required to write their own sentences.

Detailed teaching notes and guidelines are given in the following pages with suggestions on how to use the worksheets and highlighting possible areas of confusion or difficulty.

The material in 'Spotlight on Suffixes', Book Two, is very comprehensive in scope and therefore has a wide application in the classroom. The fact that the worksheets vary in difficulty and include some with a high level of vocabulary, make this a useful resource in both the upper Junior school and lower Secondary school. Knowledge about suffixing is an essential part of the National Literacy Strategy, especially in Years 4 and 5 and the material in this book would be a very useful resource for any teacher implementing this strategy. However, the worksheets generally can be used alongside any structured literacy programme, providing a useful link between spelling, word meanings and grammatical awareness. It is hoped that busy teachers will find the worksheets a useful resource to consolidate literacy work covered in the classroom and that pupils will find the worksheets challenging and enjoyable.

Gillian Aitken

TEACHING NOTES AND GUIDELINES

Section 1: Suffixing Rules   Worksheets 1-22

The first few worksheets serve as an introduction to suffixes in general. **Worksheet 1** introduces the three most common suffixes in English in the context of a story, with a creative writing task as follow-up. There are also several other suffixes in the story for recognition purposes, e.g., 'quick<u>ly</u>', 'strang<u>est</u>', 'colour<u>ful</u>', 'big<u>ger</u>', 'spring<u>y</u>', 'magic<u>al</u>', etc. **Worksheet 2** introduces seven of the most common suffixes in English for recognition purposes, and as well as working out which suffixes can be joined to which base words, attention is drawn to the distinction between vowel and consonant suffixes. This is very important for using the various suffixing rules. Generally speaking, it is much easier to adjoin consonant suffixes to base words as they are just added to the base word unless the latter ends in 'y' preceded by a consonant. The double and drop 'e' rules apply to vowel suffixes. **Worksheet 3** introduces the concept of suffixes as grammatical markers, the task being to identify each suffix as a noun, verb or adjective ending. The way each word is used in the sentences should provide enough information to classify each word. The link between suffix endings and grammatical meaning is one which is stressed throughout the book, and this kind of exercise is useful in making this link clear.

Worksheet 4 introduces the double rule. If this is a new concept to pupils, the important thing to stress is that doubling consonants protects a short vowel. Without it, the sound would be different (e.g., 'hoped' / 'hopped'). 'Spotlight on Suffixes', Book 1, gives extensive practice of all the major rules in the context of adding specific suffixes. In **Worksheet 4** the rule is stated clearly, and pupils have to add suffixes to base words by analysing the structure of the base word and deciding if the suffix begins with a vowel. This is a logical approach to understanding the rule, but in **Worksheet 4** pupils are asked to spot the doubling pattern visually, which is often the next step after understanding the rule logically. If pupils find it hard to spot the right pattern, they should be encouraged to code each word to help them recognise the $\breve{V}C|V$ pattern.

$$\text{e.g.} \quad \overset{\scriptsize\breve{v}\ c}{\text{gla}}\overset{\scriptsize c}{\text{d}} + \overset{}{\text{ness}} \qquad \overset{\scriptsize\breve{v}}{\text{hu}}\text{m} + \overset{\scriptsize c}{\text{ed}} \qquad \overset{\scriptsize v\ v}{\text{see}}\text{d} + \overset{\scriptsize v}{\text{y}}$$

When doing the sentence completion exercise, pupils should try and work out the answers mentally first, and then complete the sentences without copying them from the list above. This approach will lead to more active learning.

Worksheets 6-9b deal with the difficult concept of doubling in longer words of two or more syllables. This depends on the word stress, the basic principle being that if the final syllable has the VC pattern and is stressed, then the final consonant has to be doubled as in one-syllable words. It is almost impossible to explain this rule in a way which is comprehensible, and many pupils find it hard to identify stressed syllables. As most of the longer words which double end in 'l', 'r' or 't', the approach used in this book is to deal with each sub-group separately in the hope that this will simplify the issue. In **Worksheets 6-8**, all the words chosen must double the final consonant when adding 'ing' or 'ed'. The main difficulty for the pupils is to identify the word-meanings in these worksheets, which will stretch the more able pupils. Use of dictionaries should be encouraged. The general rule for doubling in longer words is summarised, and practice given, in **Worksheets 9a and 9b**. Teachers will have to decide for themselves whether their pupils are able to understand and apply this much more difficult rule.

The drop 'e' rule is relatively straightforward, and is generally applied successfully except when adding suffix 'y'. In these words, a common error is to keep the 'e' of the base word instead of dropping it, producing errors such as 'shiney'. Pupils should be reminded that 'y' is a vowel suffix. It also needs to be stressed that the 'e' is not dropped when adding 'ly'. (A common error is to spell words like 'extremely' without the 'e', or to put the 'e' between the 'l' and the 'y'.) **Worksheet 12** highlights the small group of words in English ending in 'ce' or 'ge' where the final 'e' must be retained in order to preserve the soft sound.

The more confusing suffixing rule which involves changing 'y' to 'i' is introduced in the context of noun plurals. **Worksheet 13a** is designed to make pupils work out the rule for themselves, while **Worksheet 13b** gives practice of the rule by means of a word-search. The general rule is summarised in **Worksheet 14** and practice given using a variety of suffixes. The change rule generally needs a great deal of practice to become automatic, as it involves paying careful attention to the structure of the base word rather than the suffix itself. The most common error is to change 'y' to 'i' unnecessarily. **Worksheet 15** highlights the fact that with many words in English, two suffixes have been added, in which case the rules are followed sequentially. The second exercise is much more difficult than merely choosing one suffix to complete a base word, but will alert pupils to the combination of double suffixes which often occur in English.

Worksheets 16-21 are rule practice sheets identical in format to the rule practice sheets in 'Spotlight on Suffixes', Book 1. Different base word and suffix combinations are used in these sheets, and the level of difficulty is graded. **Worksheets 19-21** are more difficult because for some base words, two suffixes have been added, and examples of longer words which require the doubling rule are included. **Worksheet 22** is a blank master sheet for further practice. The word lists provided as Appendices in Book 1 provide many examples of words which can be used for suffixing practice.

Section 2   a) Noun Suffixes   Worksheets 23-47

Most of the noun suffixes in English are from French and Latin. However, the suffix 'ness' (**Worksheet 23**) is from Anglo-Saxon. This suffix is given coverage in Book 1, so only one worksheet is included here. Pupils are reminded of the change 'y' to 'i' rule which may have to be applied when adding this suffix to base words.

Worksheet 24 introduces 'tion', perhaps the most common of all the noun suffix endings. Unlike the common suffixes which derive from Old English, the Latin suffixes cannot generally be taken on and off base words, but are incorporated into the structure of the word. One aim of the worksheets is to make pupils aware of related noun, verb and adjective forms which originate from the same Latin or French word. **Worksheet 24** uses two and three-syllable words and is therefore easier than **Worksheet 25** which focuses on longer words of four and five syllables. The jumbled syllable exercise in **Worksheet 25** is difficult, but pupils can be alerted to the fact that the syllable before 'tion' very often has a long vowel sound, while syllables such as 'ex', 'de' or 'mis' will be found at the beginning of words. **Worksheet 26** is a word formation exercise where the link between verb and noun forms is generally very clear. However, where a sound change has occurred such as 'inscribe' changing to 'inscription', 'destroy' changing to 'destruction' and 'receive' changing to 'reception', pupils may well be unable to find the related form without some help. This sort of exercise also lends itself to dictionary work.

Worksheets 27 and 28 focus on the related suffix 'sion'. The sound difference of this suffix, depending on the preceding letter, is highlighted in **Worksheet 26**. Pupils should notice that words with a 'ss' in the middle, such as 'discussion', have the /sh'n/ sound while a single 's' preceded by a vowel, as in 'erosion', gives the /zh'n/ sound. In **Worksheet 27** attention is drawn to related verb forms ending in 'd', 'de' and 'mit'.

Suffix 'ity' is almost as common as 'tion', and **Worksheet 29** focuses on related adjectives. Pupils should be able to find the related adjectives in the word-square without too much difficulty. The questions at the bottom of the sheet draw attention to suffixing rules as a way of revising them. It can be pointed out that even when 'ity' is added to base words (e.g., stupid → stupidity), the word stress changes, in that the syllable before 'ity' always carries the main stress. The difficulty level of **Worksheet 30** can be varied in the first exercise by adding or removing letters in the missing words.

The suffix 'ment' is another extremely common noun ending. In most cases it can be removed, leaving an intact base word. The second exercise in **Worksheet 31** is a word-search in which 20 base words are hidden to which 'ment' can be added. Pupils might need help in finding all 20 words. **Worksheet 32** draws attention to prefixes which are often found at the beginning of words with 'ment' The meanings of the various prefixes can be discussed prior to doing the worksheet.

Worksheets 33-35 deal with the related suffixes of 'ence', 'ance' and 'cy' which are from French. It is very easy to misspell words with 'ence' or 'ance' as they are pronounced in exactly the same way. However, there are more words with 'ence' than 'ance'. Words of Latin or French origin tend to be of a higher vocabulary level than the more common words originating in Anglo-Saxon, and the exercises in these sheets which involve matching meanings to words will serve as useful vocabulary extension work. Pupils should be encouraged to learn the spellings of new words as well as the meanings. The suffix 'ism' (**Worksheet 36**) is from Greek, and introduces a much higher level of vocabulary, including more abstract concepts such as 'capitalism', 'pacifism', etc. The quiz questions should challenge more able pupils. A dictionary will be essential to find all the answers. **Worksheet 37** focuses on 'age', a useful spelling pattern to teach as these words are fairly common and would be needed for writing as well as reading. Teachers can add in as many letters as they need before photocopying the worksheet to vary the level of difficulty. In the second exercise, four less common 'age' words are given. Pupils should learn the meaning and write their own sentences. Another common ending from French is 'ure' (**Worksheet 38**) which is almost always preceded by 't' or 's'. Like 'age', words ending in 'ture' or 'sure' are relatively common, and the pupils should be encouraged to learn how to spell these words. The missing vowel exercise is included because the unstressed vowels in the middle of these words makes the spelling tricky. There are not many words ending in 'tude', so it only gets a brief mention. If teachers wish to include a few more for vocabulary work, other examples are: 'altitude', 'lassitude', 'latitude', 'longitude' and 'magnitude'. **Worksheet 39** focuses on the Old English suffixes 'hood', 'ship' and 'dom' which are not very common, but nevertheless worthy of a mention. The Anglo-Saxon word and original meaning is given for general interest. Pupils might well need some help for the last anagram question!

The remaining worksheets in the noun section deal with suffixes which denote people. The most common one, of course, is 'er' (**Worksheet 40**), also included in Book 1. Pupils should be encouraged to think of their own examples before doing the worksheet as it is such a common suffix. Suffix 'or' (**Worksheet 41**) is an alternative to 'er' in words where the preceding letter is 't'. Most pupils enjoy doing the word-searches, but they should also be encouraged to learn the spellings of these words. Suffix 'ist' (**Worksheet 42**) is from Greek, and like many words of Greek origin, the vocabulary level is higher, and the spelling tricky. This worksheet is therefore aimed at more able pupils who like to be challenged. Pupils might also like to write their own questions for 'Call my Bluff' with some other 'ist' words such as 'dermatologist', 'archivist', 'entomologist', 'escapologist' or 'philatelist'. A game such as 'Call my Bluff' played in teams can liven up dictionary work, not normally viewed as a favourite classroom activity! Suffix 'an' (**Worksheet 43**) takes many forms but a special focus has been given to nationalities and words ending in 'cian'. Suffixes 'ess', 'ling' and 'ee' (**Worksheet 44**) are not very common, but lend themselves to some useful vocabulary extension work.

The last three worksheets in the noun section are practice sheets which bring together several noun suffixes for contrastive purposes, and also give practice of suffixing rules.

Section 2   b) Verb Suffixes   Worksheets 48-55

Worksheet 48 aims to raise awareness about the English tense system. The first exercise should present no difficulty, the purpose being to provide context in order to answer the questions below. The English tense system is very complex, but by doing this worksheet, the following points can be brought out:

1   There are two present tenses in English. One describes actions or events in progress or is used to express the near future. This tense (Present Continuous tense) is made by adding 'ing' to the verb stem, and using 'am', 'is' or 'are' before the verb. If the event

continued indefinitely in the past, it changes to the Past Continuous by using 'was' or 'were' before the verb stem + 'ing' as in sentence three.

The other present tense is the Simple Present tense, and it is used to describe habits, routines, permanent states or general truths. The suffix 's' is used in the third person singular form. (It can be pointed out that there were other endings in English which have disappeared. Only the 's' ending remains. Most other European languages such as French or German still have different endings.)

2 The past tense is made by adding 'ed' to verb stems, but only in regular verbs. Many common verbs are irregular, and have different past tense forms. The past tense is used for narrating events in the past, so it is the one found in stories.

The suffix 'en' was included in Book 1, but only as a verb ending meaning 'to make' or 'to become'. In **Worksheet 49** the adjectival use of 'en' as a past participle is also highlighted in the second exercise. To do this exercise, pupils have to manipulate verb forms. They might not realise that 'molten' is related to the verb 'melt'.

Suffix 'ate' is very common, and is therefore presented at two levels of difficulty. The vocabulary used in **Worksheet 50** is not very difficult, although pupils might need some help with the anagram exercise. In **Worksheet 51** longer words are used, including some 5-syllable words in the jumbled syllable exercise. As in other exercises of this kind, long vowels are marked by a macron. **Worksheet 52** focuses on 'ify', and the exercises provide scope for useful vocabulary extension work. Pupils should be reminded that when using a verb ending in 'ify' in the past tense, they should change 'y' to 'i' (e.g., fortified).

The suffix 'ise' (**Worksheets 53 and 54**) is an interesting example of how language changes. Not only has this ending undergone many changes since being borrowed into Latin and then French from Greek, but in Britain the 'ize' spelling (which reflected its Greek derivation) is being replaced by 'ise' from the French language. Most words now can be spelt with either suffix, but the 'ise' spelling is preferred. The 'ize' spelling is more restricted in that there are a few words which must be spelt 'ise' (e.g., 'exercise'). In American English, however, the 'ize' spelling has been adopted. There are many words ending in 'ise', so as with other common suffixes, there are Level 1 and Level 2 worksheets, allowing for differentiated work in the classroom. **Worksheet 54** introduces a high level of vocabulary to stretch more able pupils. **Worksheet 55** is a verb practice sheet which contrasts 'ify', 'ise' and 'ate', and gives further practice of suffixing rules.

Section 2   c) Adjective Suffixes   Worksheets 56a-78

Worksheets 56a and 56b feature the suffixes 'ing' and 'ed' as adjective endings. So far pupils have been taught that these common suffixes are verb endings, so this is a new concept to grasp. However, pupils should be aware that adjectives modify nouns, so in a phrase such as 'sleeping dog', it should be obvious that 'sleeping' is an adjective. Pupils should be made aware that 'sleeping dog' is another way of saying the dog that is sleeping', while 'buried treasure' means 'the treasure which has been buried.' There is a passive meaning in these sentences. It seemed worthwhile to give a special focus on adjectives of feeling ending in 'ed' or 'ing' (**Worksheet 56b**) as there are so many of them, making this a useful vocabulary exercise.

Suffix 'y' (**Worksheet 57**) is one of the most common adjective suffixes, and comes from Old English. It is dealt with in detail in Book 1, so here there is only worksheet on it. The focus in this worksheet is on suffixing rules, since many spelling errors occur with words ending in 'y'. Suffixes 'ful' and 'less' are also very common Old English suffixes, but again they have been introduced in Book 1, so only one worksheet (**Worksheet 58**) has been included. The level of vocabulary tends to be much lower with Old English suffixes, so there is less scope for vocabulary extension. Suffixes 'worthy', 'some', 'like' and 'ish' (**Worksheet 59**) complete the coverage of Old English suffixes. Of these, suffix 'ish' is the most common.

Worksheets 61-75 focus on adjective suffixes of Latin origin which have entered English through French. Of these, suffix 'ous' is one of the most common. **Worksheet 60** is a Level 1 worksheet presenting 15 fairly common 'ous' words in the first word completion exercise, but requiring the pupil to look up five difficult and less common words in the second exercise. **Worksheet 61** employs a much higher level of vocabulary and also requires the pupil to manipulate word forms by changing adjectives to nouns, and vice versa. **Worksheet 62** focuses on the difficult endings 'tious' and 'cious' which are often mis-spelt, and seemed to justify separate treatment. The vocabulary level is high.

The suffix 'al' is arguably the most common Latinate adjective suffix, and **Worksheet 63** is a little different from the type of worksheets presented so far in that it is an exercise on word derivations. Pupils will have the chance to learn a little Latin by doing this worksheet! This could be linked to wider work on word derivations or language change, which is always a fascinating topic. **Worksheet 64** introduces a selection of fairly common words ending in 'al' in the first exercise, while the second exercise highlights words ending in 'ical' where words of Greek origin have taken the Latin suffix. **Worksheet 65** parallels **Worksheet 62** by focusing on 'tial' and 'cial' words where the medial /sh/ sound is spelt with 'ti' or 'ci'.

Worksheets 66-69 present two more pairs of suffixes with different spellings but with identical sounds. These are best taught separately, and then brought together for contrast. Pupils can be advised to opt for the more common ending if they can't remember the correct alternative. (Suffix 'able' is a great deal more common than 'ible', and 'ent' is more common than 'ant'.)

Suffix 'ic' (**Worksheet 70**) is from Greek, and there are many words with this ending, but many of them are so obscure and specialised, that it would only cause confusion to introduce too many of them. Words ending in 'ic' are long, and lend themselves to syllable division practice as in the first exercise in **Worksheet 70**. The list of words presented in this worksheet is hopefully not too obscure. Suffix 'ive' (**Worksheets 71 and 72**) is also surprisingly common, and hence there are two levels of difficulty. **Worksheet 73** recycles 'ate', but this time as an adjective suffix where it is always unstressed and thus pronounced /ət/. The 'ə' is a phonetic symbol called 'schwa'. Finally, **Worksheets 74 and 75** present two more confusing suffix endings 'ary' and 'ory' which are also pronounced in the same way. These worksheets aim to extend vocabulary by exploring word meanings, but pupils can also be encouraged to learn spellings.

There are three adjective practice sheets (**Worksheets 76-78**) to bring together and contrast the various adjective suffixes which have been dealt with separately.

Section 2   d) Adverb Suffix 'ly'   Worksheets 79-85
and Word Formation
Practice Sheets

The suffix 'ly' was introduced in Book 1 as a verb modifier, which is its main function, and **Worksheet 79** extends understanding of this function by highlighting the use of 'ly' in narratives to add descriptive detail and generally make writing more interesting. Pupils have to think of suitable adverbs to complete sentences. They should be encouraged to be as imaginative as possible. This is an open-ended task, and if done as a class exercise, many suggestions should be forthcoming.

Worksheet 80 extends understanding of 'ly' suffix to its function as an adjective modifier, and again pupils are required to think of suitable adverbs to complete sentences. A suffixing exercise is included, as many spelling errors are made with words ending in 'ly'.

The final five worksheets are grammatical exercises in word formation, and involve the manipulation of word forms to give related nouns, verbs and adjectives. This kind of exercise demands a good level of language awareness, but if pupils have been introduced to suffixes in a systematic way, they should be able to recognise related forms without too much difficulty. They can also be taught to use a dictionary to find related parts of speech.

Suffixes

Many words in English have endings.

An ending which can be added to a word is called a <u>SUFFIX</u>.

A <u>SUFFIX</u> changes the meaning of a word.

The 3 suffixes which are most common are:

s   ing   ed

<u>Read the passage below and choose</u> s , ing <u>or</u> ed <u>to finish the words which have lost their suffix endings.</u>

<u>My Dream</u>

Last night I had a strange and vivid dream. I was fly____ through space on a magic carpet and then I land____ on a planet. I quickly jump____ off the carpet which float____ softly away. I start____ walk____ through the strangest landscape I could imagine. There were tall feathery tree____ with pink leave____ and colourful flower____ with huge, furry petal____ which were bigger than the tree____! Strange insect____ were buzz____ all around, but they were not sting____ insect____ like bee____ and I did not feel afraid. On the ground was a carpet of soft moss which was springy like a mattress. As I walk____, I bounc____ up and down higher than the tree____ and flower____, and in the distance I could see some tall, pink mountain____ with candy-floss cloud____ rest____ on top. I knew I had to climb the highest mountain in this range. It was as if I was be____ push____ along, and I felt that something wonderful and magical was go____ to happen.

Choose 5 words from the story to go in each list.

Words with S **suffix**	**Words with** ing **suffix**	**Words with** ed **suffix**
_____	_____	_____
_____	_____	_____
_____	_____	_____
_____	_____	_____
_____	_____	_____

What kind of words take the S suffix?

What kind of words take the ing or ed suffix?

Can you find 3 words in the story which have a different suffix ending?

_____   _____   _____

Now finish the story on the lines below.

_____

_____

_____

_____

_____

_____

_____

_____

_____

_____

_____

_____

_____

_____

_____

_____

Suffixes

A suffix is a letter or letters we put at the end of words to change the meaning.

The 3 most common suffixes are $\boxed{\textbf{s}}$, $\boxed{\textbf{ing}}$ and $\boxed{\textbf{ed}}$.

e.g.   book**s**
      walk**ing**
      play**ed**

How does the suffix change the meaning in each case?

Here are some other suffixes.

ful   less   ness   ly   y   er   ish

What suffixes can you add to each of the base words below?
Use the suffixes above.

1	hope	*ful, less*	9	green
2	cheap		10	quick
3	dark		11	dust
4	self		12	rich
5	risk		13	care
6	shape		14	soft
7	sad		15	rest
8	fool		16	mean

If a suffix begins with a vowel it is a <u>VOWEL</u> suffix.

(Note that $\boxed{\textbf{y}}$ is a vowel suffix.)

If a suffix begins with a consonant, it is a <u>CONSONANT</u> suffix.

Write the suffixes above in the correct list, including $\boxed{\textbf{s}}$, $\boxed{\textbf{ing}}$ and $\boxed{\textbf{ed}}$.

<u>**VOWEL suffixes**</u>   <u>**CONSONANT suffixes**</u>

Suffixes

| Suffixes give us grammatical information. From the suffix we can tell if the word is a <u>NOUN</u>, <u>VERB</u> or <u>ADJECTIVE</u>. |

<u>Circle the suffixes in the words below. There are 4 NOUN suffixes, 4 VERB suffixes and 4 ADJECTIVE suffixes.</u>

publicise   enjoyment   poisonous   inspection

foolish   entered   breakable   classify

childhood   rudeness   sharpen   dependent

<u>Now use each word to complete the sentences below. Decide whether the missing words are NOUNS, VERBS or ADJECTIVES.</u>

1   Some people do D.I.Y. for _____ as well as to save money.

2   There are no _____ spiders in Great Britain.

3   Should we _____ a tomato as a fruit or a vegetable?

4   It is not a good idea to send _____ objects in the post.

5   Everybody stood up when the Queen _____ the room.

6   It is very _____ to drink and drive.

7   The school got a very good report after its Ofsted _____.

8   The police decided to _____ the name of the wanted man.

9   After a very poor _____, he became rich and successful.

10   The girl was punished for her _____.

11   A new-born baby is totally _____ on its parents.

12   The children were told to _____ their pencils.

<u>Now put the words in the correct list below.</u>

<u>NOUN suffix</u>	<u>VERB suffix</u>	<u>ADJECTIVE suffix</u>
_____	_____	_____
_____	_____	_____
_____	_____	_____
_____	_____	_____

The Double Rule

In the English spelling system, a double consonant keeps the vowel short.

e.g. hŏpping
fĭtted
rĕddish

When we add a VOWEL suffix to a word with ONE syllable, ONE short vowel, and ending in ONE consonant, we must DOUBLE the final consonant of the base word to keep the vowel short.

e.g. rŭn + ing = running

Look at the base words below.
For each one ask yourself the following 4 questions:

1 Does the base word have ONE syllable?
2 Does the base word have ONE short vowel?
3 Does the base word end in ONE consonant?
4 Is the suffix a VOWEL suffix?

If the answer is YES to all these questions, use the DOUBLE rule.
If the answer is NO to any question, JUST ADD the suffix.

WORD SUM	DOUBLE	JUST ADD	RESULT
1 fun + y	4	7	funny
2 rain + ed			
3 blot + ing			
4 stab + ed			
5 sulk + y			
6 hop + ing			
7 nut + y			
8 fat + ness			
9 sip + ed			
10 sun + less			
11 thin + er			
12 dream + y			
13 spit + ing			
14 feel + ing			
15 red + ish			

Double Rule: V̆C|V

Circle all the word-sums below which require the Double rule.
Look for the VC|V pattern. There are 15 altogether.

glad + ness   hum + ed   fun + y

drop + ful   sun + less   run + ing

seed + y   jog + er   heat + ed

feel + ing   mud + y   rob + er

dream + ed   skin + y   shop + ful

win + er   mend + ed   trip + ed

fit + er   sand + y   end + less

wag + ed   flop + y   fat + ness

bag + y   book + ed   pat + ed

risk + y   tip + ed   self + ish

Now write each word out below. Remember to double the final consonant of the base word.

1 _____   6 _____   11 _____

2 _____   7 _____   12 _____

3 _____   8 _____   13 _____

4 _____   9 _____   14 _____

5 _____   10 _____   15 _____

Now complete the sentences below by choosing one of the above words.

1   The _____ _____ over a fallen branch and fell into a _____ puddle.

2   The _____ of the _____ contest was older but _____ than all the other competitors.

3   The _____ dog _____ its tail when it was _____.

4   The old woman looked very _____ in her _____ trousers and _____ hat.

5   The _____ _____ a tune as he calmly _____ the contents of the safe into his bag.

Double Rule in longer words: Words ending in 'l'

Rule

Longer words ending in 'l' preceded by a vowel double the 'l' of the base word when adding a VOWEL suffix.

e.g.   trave$\underline{l}$ + $\overset{v}{e}$r = traveller
control + $\overset{v}{i}$ng = controlled
disti$\underline{l}$ + $\overset{v}{e}$d = distilled

But: Do NOT double if the final 'l' of the base word is preceded by a double vowel or when adding a consonant suffix.

e.g.   conc$\underline{ea}$l + ed   = concealed **(JUST ADD)**
fulfil + $\overset{c}{\underline{m}}$ent = fulfilment **(JUST ADD)**

Add suffixes to the words below, doubling 'l' when necessary.

dishevel + ed = _____   enrol   + ment = _____

appeal   + ing = _____   propel +   er = _____

recoil   + ed = _____   quarrel + some = _____

patrol   + ing = _____   pedal   +   ed = _____

marvel   + ous = _____   fulfil   +   ed = _____

repel   + ent = _____   prevail +   ing = _____

Now choose 3 of the above words which doubled the final 'l', and use them in sentences of your own.

_____

_____

_____

_____

_____

_____

_____

Double Rule in longer words: Words ending in 'r'

Rule

2-syllable words ending in 'r' preceded by a single vowel double the final 'r' of the base word when adding a vowel suffix.

e.g.   prefer + ĕd = preferred

In these words the final syllable is stressed.
The doubling is to protect the short vowel.
Most of these words end in 'cur', 'fer' or 'ter'.

Do NOT double if the final syllable is unstressed.

e.g.   súffer + ed = suffered

Read the words below which all end in 'r' preceded by a single vowel. The final syllable is stressed.

| abhor | inter | prefer | transfer | refer |
| deter | incur | recur | occur | infer |

Now match each word to the meanings given below.

	Base word	**Meaning**
e.g.	*deter*	To hinder or prevent someone from doing something.
a)	_____	To send on or direct to some authority; to turn or go to for information, etc.
b)	_____	To bring upon oneself, e.g., debt, blame, etc.
c)	_____	To bury.
d)	_____	To like more than something or somebody else.
e)	_____	To happen.

f) _____ To regard with disgust and hatred.

g) _____ To happen again.

h) _____ To reach an opinion from facts or reasoning.

i) _____ To convey, transmit, hand over etc. from one person, place etc. to another.

Now add the suffixes to the base word.
Remember to double the final 'r' of the base word.

1 inter + ed = _____   6 transfer + ed = _____

2 infer + ed = _____   7 recur + ing = _____

3 incur + ed = _____   8 deter + ent = _____

4 refer + ed = _____   9 prefer + ed = _____

5 occur + ed = _____   10 abhor + ence = _____

Now use each word to complete the sentences below.

1 The man _____ a lot of debts by gambling.

2 After 6 months working in the same bank, she was _____ to another branch.

3 The questionnaire asked me what my _____ holiday destination was.

4 A jail sentence is seen as a _____ to stop people from committing serious crime.

5 Human remains were found _____ in the walls of the castle.

6 The teacher _____ from the guilty look on the boy's face that he had not done his homework.

7 Although the fire had _____ several years ago, she still had _____ nightmares about it.

8 He _____ to his dictionary to check the spelling of 'encyclopaedia'.

9 Most people regard snakes and large, hairy spiders with _____.

Double Rule in longer words: Words ending in 't'

Rule

2-syllable words ending in 't' preceded by a single vowel double the final 't' of the base word when adding a vowel suffix.

e.g.   admiť + ěd = admitted

In these words the final syllable is stressed. The doubling is to protect the short vowel.

Do NOT double if the final syllable is unstressed.

e.g.   débit + ed = debited

Read the words below which all end in 't' preceded by a single vowel. The final syllable is stressed.

commit   emit   omit   permit   submit   transmit

remit   abet   regret   upset   outfit   acquit

Which word means?

a) To give or send out heat, light, etc.   _____

b) To help someone in a crime.   _____

c) To send or pass on to another person, place or thing.   _____

d) To send money by post; to let someone off a punishment or debt.   _____

e) To fail to do something; to leave out.   _____

f) To declare not guilty of a crime.   _____

g) To give in to someone or something; to surrender.   _____

h) To do or carry out an act or a crime.   _____

i) To allow.   _____

j) To cause distress to someone or something. _____

k) To equip; to sell men's clothes. _____

l) To feel sorry for something one has done. _____

Now add the suffixes to the base word.
Remember to double the final 't' of the base word.

1 commit + ed = _____   7 upset + ing = _____

2 emit   + ed = _____   8 remit + ed = _____

3 omit   + ed = _____   9 regret + ed = _____

4 permit   + ing = _____   10 outfit   + er = _____

5 submit + ed = _____   11 abet   + ing = _____

6 transmit + ed = _____   12 acquit + ed = _____

Now use each word to complete the sentences below.

1   A sum of £500 was _____ to my bank account.

2   After a long trial the man was _____ of murder.

3   If someone is found guilty of aiding and _____ a crime, he or she can go to prison.

4   An _____ is someone who sells men's clothes.

5   They decided to go for a long hike, weather _____.

6   The message was _____ by e-mail.

7   The volcano _____ a huge cloud of ash and smoke before the eruption died down.

8   The police were surprised to find out that the burglary had been _____ by an 85-year-old man.

9   The boy _____ not working harder when he received his poor examination results.

10 The girl failed her English examination because she _____ to do the last question.

11 It is _____ to see somebody hurt or in pain.

12 The terrorists finally _____ to the police after holding out for 10 days with 6 hostages.

Doubling in longer words: General Rule

Rule

In words of more than one syllable ending in <u>ONE</u> consonant preceded by <u>ONE</u> short vowel, you must use the <u>DOUBLE</u> rule if the last syllable is stressed.

e.g. omít + ed = omi<u>tt</u>ed **(DOUBLE because the last syllable is stressed)**

crédit + ed = credited **(JUST ADD because the last syllable is <u>NOT</u> stressed)**

Divide each base word into syllables. Mark the stressed syllable. Then add the suffix, doubling where necessary.

1 commit + ed = _____

2 prefer + ed = _____

3 equip + ed = _____

4 differ + ent = _____

5 develop + ing = _____

6 begin + ing = _____

7 regret + ed = _____

8 prefer + ence = _____

9 benefit + ed = _____

10 admit + ed = _____

11 recur + ing = _____

12 inhabit + ed = _____

Now use each of the words which doubled in the sentences below.

1 The man who _____ the bank robbery was given a jail sentence.

2 The _____ of the film was very dramatic.

3 The child _____ his bad behaviour when he saw how upset his mother was.

4 They set off on the hike _____ for all kinds of weather.

5 The woman was _____ to hospital for tests.

6 Most people's _____ hand for writing is their right one.

7 A _____ nightmare is one which keeps coming back.

Doubling in longer words: General Rule

Rule

Do NOT double if:

1. **The final syllable contains 2 vowels before the last consonant.**

   e.g. der$\overset{vv}{ai}$l + ed = derailed   **(JUST ADD the suffix)**

2. **You are adding a CONSONANT suffix.**

   e.g. commit + $\overset{c}{m}$ent = commitment   **(JUST ADD the suffix)**

Use all the rules you have learnt about doubling in longer words to do the word-sums below.

You must follow the DOUBLE rule for 11 of the words, and JUST ADD for the remaining 9.

1	begin + ing = _____	11	refer + ed = _____
2	permit + ing = _____	12	admit + ed = _____
3	suffer + ing = _____	13	plummet + ed = _____
4	restrain + ed = _____	14	equip + ment = _____
5	acquit + al = _____	15	marvel + ous = _____
6	forgot + en = _____	16	enrol + ment = _____
7	repeat + ed = _____	17	regret + ed = _____
8	rebel + ed = _____	18	profit + ed = _____
9	redeem + ed = _____	19	upset + ing = _____
10	appeal + ing = _____	20	model + ing = _____

Score _____

20

The Drop 'e' Rule

Rule

If you are adding a <u>VOWEL</u> suffix to a base word ending in 'e', you must <u>DROP</u> the 'e'.

e.g. lik<u>e</u> + ing = liking

But: **If you are adding a <u>CONSONANT</u> suffix, do <u>NOT</u> drop the 'e'.**

e.g. spit<u>e</u> + ful = spit<u>e</u>ful

Do the word-sums below, dropping the 'e' where necessary.
Remember that 'y' is a vowel suffix.

1 flame + ing = _____

2 excite + ment = _____

3 hope + less = _____

4 haze + y = _____

5 ice + y = _____

6 escape + ing = _____

7 rude + ness = _____

8 life + less = _____

9 grate + ful = _____

10 precise + ly = _____

11 doze + ing = _____

12 time + less = _____

13 laze + y = _____

14 trade + er = _____

15 peace + ful = _____

16 shine + y = _____

17 extreme + ly = _____

18 care + ful = _____

19 refuse + ing = _____

20 hide + ing = _____

Score _____

20

Drop 'e' Rule

Do the word-sums below, dropping the 'e' of the base word when necessary.

manage + ment = _____   spike + y = _____

struggle + ing = _____   rude + ness = _____

extreme + ly = _____   inhale + ing = _____

continue + ous = _____   taste + ed = _____

stare + ing = _____   require + ed = _____

ice + y = _____   complete + ly = _____

sincere + ly = _____   survive + or = _____

bereave + ment = _____   bore + dom = _____

comrade + ship = _____   surprise + ing = _____

excite + ment = _____   wheeze + ing = _____

Now use the 10 words which dropped the 'e' of the base word to complete the sentences below.

1   The _____s of the earthquake _____ basic food and shelter.

2   It was _____ to see the sun come out after 8 hours of _____ rain.

3   After _____ the toxic fumes, the workers started _____, coughing and fighting for breath.

4   The child could not stop _____ at the man with dyed purple, _____ hair.

5   Everybody was _____ to stay upright on the _____ pavements which had frozen solid in the night.

Drop 'e' Rule: Soft 'c' and 'g' words

Rule

If you are adding suffixes ous **or** able **to words ending in 'ce' or 'ge' making a soft sound, do NOT drop the 'e' or the sound will become hard.**

e.g.   noti<u>ce</u> + able = notic<u>ea</u>ble

courage + ous   = courag<u>eo</u>us

Note: prestige + ous = prestig<u>io</u>us **(Final 'e' changed to 'i')**

Do the word-sums below by just adding the suffix. Do NOT drop the 'e'.

manage   + able = _____   outrage   + ous = _____

pronounce + able = _____   irreplace   + able = _____

advantage + ous = _____   service   + able = _____

enforce   + able = _____   trace   + able = _____

marriage   + able = _____   gorge   + ous = _____

peace   + able = _____   knowledge + able = _____

Now use 8 of the above words to complete the sentences below.

1 If a law is not _____, it is useless.

2 Everybody was shocked at the child's _____ behaviour
   at the party.

3 The fridge was old but still _____.

4 The word was so long that it was un _____.

5 In some countries girls of 15 or less are considered of
   _____ age.

6 Teachers should be _____ about their subjects.

7 It is _____ to get to the Sales early if you want a bargain.

8 Great works of Art are _____ if they are damaged or stolen.

Nouns ending in 'y': Plural forms

What is different about the words in List A to the words in List B?

List A	List B
play	lady
essay	jelly
toy	ruby
convoy	party
osprey	army
key	century
guy	cry
buy	enemy

How do you make these words plural?

Rule

For List A words

_____

_____

For List B words

_____

_____

Nouns ending in 'y': Plural forms

> **If there is a <u>VOWEL</u> before the final 'y', <u>JUST ADD</u> 's'.** e.g. toy<u>s</u>
>
> **If there is a <u>CONSONANT</u> before the final 'y', <u>CHANGE</u> 'y' to 'i'**
> **and add suffix 'es'.** e.g. bab<u>ies</u>

Find 25 NOUNS in the word-square below which end in 'y'.
Write out each word and make it PLURAL by adding the correct suffix.
(Words go ACROSS and DOWN only.)

a	c	o	m	e	d	y	t	v	s	t
j	e	r	s	e	y	d	r	a	e	r
e	n	q	u	i	r	y	a	r	n	o
s	t	b	p	u	p	p	y	m	t	l
s	u	p	a	r	t	y	g	y	r	l
a	r	o	s	c	o	u	n	t	y	e
y	y	n	t	o	y	d	u	t	y	y
g	u	y	r	n	y	l	a	d	y	b
p	l	a	y	v	a	l	l	e	y	o
r	u	b	y	o	m	o	n	k	e	y
a	b	b	e	y	k	i	d	n	e	y

Word	Plural form		Word	Plural form
e.g. *abbey*	*abbeys*		l _ _ _	_____
a _ _ _	_____		m _ _ _ _ _	_____
b _ _	_____		p _ _ _ _	_____
c _ _ _ _ _ _	_____		p _ _ _ _ _	_____
c _ _ _ _ _	_____		p _ _ _	_____
c _ _ _ _ _	_____		p _ _ _ _	_____
c _ _ _ _ _	_____		p _ _ _ _	_____
d _ _ _	_____		r _ _ _	_____
e _ _ _ _ _	_____		s _ _ _ _ _	_____
e _ _ _ _ _ _	_____		t _ _	_____
g _ _	_____		tr _ _	_____
j _ _ _ _ _	_____		tr _ _ _ _ _	_____
k _ _ _ _ _	_____		v _ _ _ _ _	_____

Adding suffixes to words ending in 'y'

Rule

If the suffix is ing , JUST ADD the suffix.

e.g. display + ing = displaying
supply + ing = supplying

For ALL other suffixes, look at the structure of the BASE WORD.

If there is a CONSONANT before the 'y', CHANGE 'y' to 'i'.

e.g. deny + ed = denied
empty + ness = emptiness

If there is a VOWEL before the final 'y', JUST ADD the suffix.

e.g. employ + er = employer
replay + ed = replayed

Do the word-sums below by following the correct rule.

1	spray	+ s = _____		16	hurry	+ ed = _____
2	defy	+ ed = _____		17	stray	+ ed = _____
3	reply	+ ing = _____		18	employ	+ ing = _____
4	dismay	+ ed = _____		19	fancy	+ ful = _____
5	portray	+ ed = _____		20	levy	+ ed = _____
6	deploy	+ ment = _____		21	journey	+ ed = _____
7	survey	+ or = _____		22	lazy	+ ness = _____
8	buy	+ er = _____		23	weary	+ some = _____
9	party	+ es = _____		24	melody	+ ous = _____
10	magnify	+ ed = _____		25	betray	+ al = _____
11	repay	+ ing = _____		26	industry	+ al = _____
12	dusty	+ est = _____		27	glory	+ ous = _____
13	duty	+ ful = _____		28	merry	+ ment = _____
14	rely	+ able = _____		29	bury	+ ing = _____
15	copy	+ ing = _____		30	envy	+ able = _____

Adding 2 suffixes to base words

Rule

When adding 2 suffixes to base words, follow the rules one at a time. e.g. skin + y + est

Step 1:   skin + y   = ski<u>nn</u>y   **(DOUBLE)**

Step 2:   skinny + est = skinn<u>i</u>est   **(CHANGE 'y' to 'i')**

Add the suffixes to the base words below.

1 regret   + ful   + ly   = _____

2 cream   + y   + er   = _____

3 fun   + y   + ly   = _____

4 fat   + en   + ing   = _____

5 surprise + ing   + ly   = _____

6 time   + less + ness   = _____

7 prude   + ish   + ness   = _____

8 convince + ing   + ly   = _____

Choose 2 suffixes from the box below to add to each base word. Remember to follow the correct rules.

ing	ed	est	less	y	ful	en	ness	ish	ly

1 drunk   + _____ + _____ = _____

2 sleep   + _____ + _____ = _____

3 greed   + _____ + _____ = _____

4 wealth + _____ + _____ = _____

5 hurry   + _____ + _____ = _____

6 deaf   + _____ + _____ = _____

7 fool   + _____ + _____ = _____

8 grace   + _____ + _____ = _____

Rule Practice Sheet

(DOUBLE?)   (DROP 'e'?)   (CHANGE 'y' to 'i'?)   (JUST ADD?)

Use the correct suffixing rule to add the suffixes to the base words below.

BASE WORD	SUFFIX	RULE	RESULT
healthy	er		
shun	ed		
Dane	ish		
grumble	ing		
journey	ed		
knot	y		
lorry	es		
nerve	y		
cheer	ful		
trot	ing		
heavy	ness		
cool	est		
flat	en		
amaze	ment		
sag	ing		
fancy	ed		
wheeze	ing		
awake	en		
duty	ful		
room	y		

Rule Practice Sheet

{ DOUBLE? } { DROP 'e'? } { CHANGE 'y' to 'i'? } { JUST ADD? }

Use the correct suffixing rule to add the suffixes to the base words below.

BASE WORD	SUFFIX	RULE	RESULT
operate	ing		
age	less		
trim	ed		
copy	ed		
inhale	ing		
body	ly		
chat	y		
array	ed		
tickle	ish		
tasty	est		
throb	ing		
pastry	es		
wet	ish		
weep	y		
judge	ing		
thud	ed		
refine	ment		
taste	y		
mean	er		
ugly	ness		

Rule Practice Sheet

{ DOUBLE? } { DROP 'e'? } { CHANGE 'y' to 'i'? } { JUST ADD? }

Use the correct suffixing rule to add the suffixes to the base words below.

BASE WORD	SUFFIX	RULE	RESULT
annoy	ing		
delete	ing		
grain	y		
spin	ing		
clumsy	ness		
crag	y		
busy	est		
vet	ed		
rogue	ish		
multiply	ed		
bubble	y		
flab	y		
foam	ing		
surprise	ing		
step	ing		
windy	er		
haste	en		
plenty	ful		
portray	ed		
extreme	ly		

Rule Practice Sheet

{ DOUBLE? }　{ DROP 'e'? }　{ CHANGE 'y' to 'i'? }　{ JUST ADD? }

Use the correct suffixing rule to add the suffixes to the base words below.

BASE WORD	SUFFIX	RULE	RESULT
friendly	est		
fret	ing		
notice	able		
postpone	ing		
dreary	ness		
guilt	y + ly		
whip	ed		
sincere	ity		
control	ed		
examine	ing		
orbit	ed		
survey	or		
grudge	ing + ly		
conspiracy	es		
excite	able		
mystify	ing		
noise	y + est		
chop	y		
bleed	ing		
emit	ed		

Rule Practice Sheet

{ DOUBLE? }   { DROP 'e'? }   { CHANGE 'y' to 'i'? }   { JUST ADD? }

Use the correct suffixing rule to add the suffixes to the base words below.

BASE WORD	SUFFIX	RULE	RESULT
deplore	able		
approve	al		
prefer	ed		
argue	ing		
taste	y + er		
squat	er		
advertise	ment		
upset	ing		
bit	y		
glory	ous		
pity	ful + ly		
receive	ing		
edit	or		
signal	ed		
star	y		
drunk	en + ness		
industry	al		
fun	y + ly		
wrinkle	y		
weary	some		

Rule Practice Sheet

{ **DOUBLE?** } { **DROP 'e'?** } { **CHANGE 'y' to 'i'?** } { **JUST ADD?** }

Use the correct suffixing rule to add the suffixes to the base words below.

BASE WORD	SUFFIX	RULE	RESULT
testify	ed		
occur	ed		
lively	hood		
sleep	less + ness		
persevere	ing		
gossip	ing		
comrade	ship		
confuse	ing + ly		
enforce	able		
expel	ed		
celebrity	es		
laze	y + ly		
crumble	y		
courage	ous		
severe	ity		
equip	ed		
justify	ed		
gallop	ing		
defy	ance		
complete	ing		

Rule Practice Sheet

{ DOUBLE? } { DROP 'e'? } { CHANGE 'y' to 'i'? } { JUST ADD? }

Use the correct suffixing rule to add the suffixes to the base words below.

BASE WORD	SUFFIX	RULE	RESULT

Suffix ness

This is a common **NOUN** suffix from old English 'nes' meaning state or condition. e.g. dark<u>ness</u>, blind<u>ness</u>.

It changes an **ADJECTIVE** into a **NOUN**.

Words ending in ness are **ABSTRACT NOUNS** because you can't see, touch or hear things like 'happi<u>ness</u>', 'mad<u>ness</u>'.

Rule

In most cases you **JUST ADD** ness to the base word because it is a **CONSONANT** suffix.

But if the base word ends in 'y' with a consonant before it, you must change 'y' to 'i'. e.g. empt<u>y</u> + ness = empt<u>i</u>ness

<u>Rule Breakers:</u>   Note that with 'shyness', 'slyness' and 'dryness', the suffix is just added.

Add ness to the base words below.

1 coarse   + ness = _____
2 dry   + ness = _____
3 clumsy + ness = _____
4 idle   + ness = _____
5 drunken + ness = _____

6 calm   + ness = _____
7 open + ness = _____
8 gentle + ness = _____
9 easy   + ness = _____
10 tidy   + ness = _____

Word Quiz: Write down the NOUN ending in ness to describe the state, condition or feeling described below.

1 A feeling of being by oneself.   l _ _ _ _ _ ness

2 What you will feel if you go round and round.   d _ _ _ _ ness

3 You might feel this if you go away from home.   h _ _ _ _ _ _ _ ness

4 A memory problem.   f _ _ _ _ _ _ _ _ ness

5 New-born babies are in this state.   h _ _ _ _ _ _ _ ness

6 Good manners.   p _ _ _ _ _ ness

7 When there is no movement.   s _ _ _ _ ness

8 A problem seeing things far away.   s _ _ _ _ _ _ _ _ _ _ _ ness

9 Feeling you will experience in space.   w _ _ _ _ _ _ _ _ _ ness

10 When you faint, you will lose this.   c _ _ _ _ _ _ _ _ _ ness

Suffix tion

Many **NOUNS** in English end in tion . These words came originally from Latin but came into English from French.

Words ending in tion are normally **ABSTRACT NOUNS**.

Unscramble the letters below to find 10 words ending in tion **to match the meanings. Each word will have 2 syllables.**

1 o t s n q u e i _____ If you ask one, you expect an answer.

2 u o i a t c n _____ A type of sale where the goods go to the person who bids the most.

3 n c f t i i o _____ Story books.

4 n o d t i i c _____ Way of speaking or pronouncing words.

5 o t i n p o _____ Liquid medicine or poison.

6 i m t o o n _____ Movement.

7 o o t i n n _____ Idea.

8 o t r a c i f n _____ A part of a whole.

9 n t o l i o _____ Ointment.

10 n t r o a i _____ Your share when there is only a little to go around.

Choose a 3-syllable word ending in tion **to complete the sentences below.** *(The first letter has been given to help you.)*

1 The e _ _ _ tion of the volcano caused a lot of damage.

2 He looked at his r _ _ _ _ _ tion in the mirror.

3 If there is not enough food, people die of s _ _ _ _ _ tion.

4 The selfish boy had no i _ _ _ _ tion of sharing his sweets.

5 In an e _ _ _ tion people vote for a new government.

6 He was very proud of his stamp c _ _ _ _ _ tion.

7 The school got a good report after its Ofsted i _ _ _ _ _ tion.

8 The girl's a _ _ _ tion was to be a doctor.

9 Many old people get chest i _ _ _ _ tions in the winter.

10 The cooker was old but it was still in good c _ _ _ _ tion.

11 The boy got told off for not paying a _ _ _ _ tion in class.

12 A v _ _ _ tion is a holiday, but a v _ _ _ tion is a job.

Suffix tion

Choose a 4-syllable word ending in **tion** **to complete the sentences below.** *(The first letter has been given to help you.)*

1 He was so tired that he began to lose c _ _ _ _ _ _ _ _tion during the exam.

2 In the French R _ _ _ _ _tion many rich people were executed or had to flee the country.

3 He made a good recovery from his heart o _ _ _ _tion.

4 China and India both have very big p _ _ _ _tions.

5 She answered the difficult question without any h _ _ _ _ _tion.

6 The plane did not reach its d _ _ _ _ _ _tion due to bad weather.

7 The v _ _ _ _ _ _tion programme was too late to prevent an epidemic.

8 There was no i _ _ _ _ _tion to suggest that the child was ill.

9 A wedding is a cause for c _ _ _ _ _ _tion.

10 He made fifty job a _ _ _ _ _ _tions before he found employment.

11 The Christmas d _ _ _ _ _tions were much admired.

12 There was no e _ _ _ _ _ _tion for the child's strange behaviour.

Re-arrange the syllables below to make 12 words ending in tion.

(If the vowel has a long sound, the symbol ¯ has been used.)

1 nā tion ex i am _____

2 il civ ī tion sā _____

3 nā si as tion sas _____

4 com ac tion dā mō _____

5 mū tion cā com ni _____

6 bar dis cā tion em _____

7 as ex ā tion per _____

8 doc men tion ū tā _____

9 tion in ti ves gā _____

10 gan or ī tion sā _____

11 pā oc tion cū prē _____

12 tion mi dē nā ter _____

Which syllable is stressed in the above words?

Suffix tion

Many NOUNS ending in tion have a related verb.

	VERB	NOUN
e.g.	attend	attention
	consider	consideration

Give the NOUN ending in tion which is related to the VERBS below.
(Use a dictionary to check those you are not sure of.)

VERB	NOUN	VERB	NOUN
alter	_____	apply	_____
create	_____	confirm	_____
donate	_____	qualify	_____
instruct	_____	oppose	_____
introduce	_____	observe	_____
rotate	_____	produce	_____
attend	_____	restore	_____
hesitate	_____	revolve	_____
contemplate	_____	imitate	_____
inscribe	_____	destroy	_____

Give the verb which is related to the NOUNS ending in tion below.

VERB	NOUN	VERB	NOUN
_____	exhibition	_____	relaxation
_____	recognition	_____	execution
_____	devotion	_____	description
_____	restoration	_____	reduction
_____	purification	_____	communication
_____	interrogation	_____	assassination
_____	deprivation	_____	examination
_____	inflation	_____	revelation
_____	ignition	_____	obligation
_____	reception	_____	prescription

Suffix sion

Some NOUNS end in sion instead of tion .

Words ending in sion can have 2 sounds.

In some words the suffix can sound /sh'n/.   e.g. pas<u>sion</u>
In other words the suffix can sound /zh'n/.   e.g. vi<u>sion</u>

Read the words below. Then put them in the correct list.

discussion   erosion   conclusion   mansion
decision   confusion   impression   pension   occasion
confession   collision   procession

sh'n   **zh'n**

_____ _____   _____ _____

_____ _____   _____ _____

_____ _____   _____ _____

Now use each word to complete the sentences below.

1 A wedding is a very special _____.

2 He retired on a very small _____.

3 The man's _____ led to his arrest for murder.

4 We got the _____ that the couple were very rich because
   they lived in a _____.

5 The serious _____ between the bus and the lorry blocked
   the motorway for several hours.

6 Some indecisive people find it hard to make _____s.

7 During the festival, a long _____ of people walked through the
   village to the church.

8 The _____ about whether to widen the road or not reached
   no satisfactory _____.

9 The instructions were not clear and caused a lot of _____.

10 When the earth's surface is worn away by wind and rain, this process
    is called _____.

sion Related NOUNS and VERBS

With many **NOUNS** ending in sion, the related **VERB** form is obvious.

e.g. discu**ssion** **VERB** = discuss

disper**sion** **VERB** = disperse

But look at the **VERB** stems below which have related **NOUNS** ending in sion.

a) exten**d** ⟶ exten**sion** ('d' ⟶ 'sion')
b) delu**de** ⟶ delu**sion** ('de' ⟶ 'sion')
c) ad**mit** ⟶ admi**ssion** ('mit' ⟶ 'sion')

Change the VERBS below into NOUNS.

VERB	NOUN	VERB	NOUN
1 comprehend	_____	6 remit	_____
2 explode	_____	7 suspend	_____
3 commit	_____	8 omit	_____
4 expand	_____	9 persuade	_____
5 invade	_____	10 permit	_____

Now use each NOUN ending in sion to complete the sentences below.

1 There was a huge _____ when the bomb went off.

2 The pupil's disruptive behaviour led to his _____ from school.

3 The salesman received 10% _____ on every car he sold.

4 If cancer is not spreading, it is said to be in _____.

5 His _____ of French was very good, but his speaking skills were poor.

6 When people keep phoning you at home, it is an _____ of privacy.

7 The rapid _____ of his business soon made him very rich.

8 Forgetting to include the Lord Mayor on the guest list was a serious _____.

9 Successful salesmen are very good in the art of _____.

10 Her parents would not give her _____ to go to the party.

ity Related NOUNS and ADJECTIVES

The suffix ity is the next most common **NOUN** suffix after tion.

Words ending in ity are derived from Latin but have mostly entered the English language through French.

Most ity words have a related **ADJECTIVE** form.

	NOUN	**ADJECTIVE**
e.g.	density	dense
	publicity	public

In the word-square below find 15 ADJECTIVES which match the

NOUNS ending in ity . *(Words go ACROSS and DOWN only.)*

a	s	e	c	u	r	e	f	v	o
f	i	a	c	t	i	v	e	i	s
p	m	b	v	a	i	n	s	s	t
o	p	l	c	h	v	k	t	i	u
s	l	e	q	u	a	l	i	b	p
s	e	n	o	b	l	e	v	l	i
i	j	o	l	l	y	q	e	e	d
b	m	a	t	u	r	e	b	r	d
l	e	c	u	r	i	o	u	s	u
e	g	e	n	e	r	o	u	s	z

	NOUN	**ADJECTIVE**
1	ability	_____
2	activity	_____
3	curiosity	_____
4	equality	_____
5	festivity	_____
6	generosity	_____
7	jollity	_____
8	maturity	_____
9	nobility	_____
10	possibility	_____
11	security	_____
12	simplicity	_____
13	stupidity	_____
14	vanity	_____
15	visibility	_____

QUESTIONS

Can you find 2 ADJECTIVES which drop 'e' when adding 'ity'?

_____ _____

Can you find 2 ADJECTIVES which Just Add 'ity'?

_____ _____

Can you find an ADJECTIVE which changes 'y' to 'i' when adding 'ity'?

_____

What happens to ADJECTIVES ending in 'ble' when 'ity' is added?

'ble' ⟶ _____

49

Suffix ity

Complete the NOUNS ending in ity in the sentences below.

(The first letter and one or two others have been given to help you.)

1 Fridges are now considered a n _ c _ _ _ ity, but there were none a hundred years ago.

2 He had a poor record for p _ n _ _ u _ lity because he found it difficult to get up in the mornings.

3 She was given every o _ _ o _ t _ _ ity to develop her musical talent, but nothing came of it.

4 Because of her outgoing and friendly p _ _ _ _ n _ _ ity, Sally was very popular at school.

5 Teenagers often rebel against the a _ _ h _ rity of their parents.

6 They say that c _ _ i _ _ ity killed the cat!

7 The police did not reveal the i _ e _ _ ity of the murder victim.

8 Many people think it is cruel to keep wild animals in c _ p _ _ _ ity.

9 The family lived in a poor l _ c _ _ ity on the edge of the city.

10 When you buy a lottery ticket, you only have a small p _ _ b _ _ _ _ ity of winning.

Make NOUNS ending in ity from the ADJECTIVES below.

ADJECTIVE	NOUN	ADJECTIVE	NOUN
1 diverse		9 insane	
2 simple		10 normal	
3 dignified		11 pompous	
4 prosperous		12 severe	
5 complex		13 regular	
6 real		14 flexible	
7 futile		15 obscure	
8 fertile		16 atrocious	

Suffix ment

> The suffix **ment** is another very common **NOUN** suffix which derives from Latin and has entered English through French.
>
> The suffix normally changes a **VERB** into a **NOUN**.
>
> | **VERB** | **NOUN** |
> |---|---|
> | e.g. enjoy | enjoyment |

Match the words below ending in ment to the correct meaning.

astonishment   nourishment   fulfilment   compliment
environment   accomplishment   elopement   requirement
achievement   imprisonment   bewilderment

1 What you may face if convicted of a crime.   _____

2 A polite expression of praise.   _____

3 Two words meaning something that has been completed successfully.   _____ _____

4 Physical surroundings.   _____

5 Food which sustains the body.   _____

6 When a young couple run away secretly to get married.   _____

7 Confusion.   _____

8 Something you need.   _____

9 Great surprise.   _____

10 Feeling of satisfaction.   _____

Find 20 words in the square below to which you can add suffix ment.

a	g	r	e	e	k	s	h	i	p
r	e	p	u	n	i	s	h	q	o
r	m	a	d	e	p	a	r	t	d
a	p	y	f	i	t	m	o	v	e
n	l	g	j	e	q	u	i	p	v
g	o	v	e	r	n	s	e	t	e
e	y	s	t	a	t	e	n	r	l
j	u	d	g	e	o	d	d	e	o
c	m	a	n	a	g	e	o	a	p
r	e	f	r	e	s	h	w	t	y

(Words go ACROSS and DOWN only.)

1 a _ _ _ _   11 j _ _ _ _

2 a _ _ _ _   12 m _ _ _ _ _

3 a _ _ _ _ _ _   13 m _ _ _

4 d _ _ _ _   14 o _ _ _

5 d _ _ _ _ _ _   15 p _ _

6 e _ _ _ _   16 p _ _ _

7 e _ _ _ _   17 r _ _ _ _ _ _

8 e _ _ _ _   18 s _ _ _

9 f _ _   19 s _ _ _ _

10 g _ _ _ _ _   20 t _ _ _ _

Suffix ment

Many words with ment have **PREFIXES** at the beginning.
These prefixes are from Latin.

e.g. <u>re</u>settlement = settling again
<u>mal</u>nourishment = bad nourishment
<u>dis</u>agreement = not in agreement

Complete the words below by choosing from the prefixes in the box.
(Use a dictionary if you are not sure which prefix to choose.)

con   com   de   dis   en   im   in
mal   mis   re   under   post   em   ex

1 _____government	9 _____vestment	17 _____mitment
2 _____armament	10 _____adjustment	18 _____ponement
3 _____prisonment	11 _____ployment	19 _____campment
4 _____development	12 _____inforcement	20 _____couragement
5 _____tachment	13 _____citement	21 _____treatment
6 _____tentment	14 _____alignment	22 _____peachment
7 _____cealment	15 _____gagement	23 _____pairment
8 _____statement	16 _____partment	24 _____plement

QUIZ: Which word means?

1 Damage or weakness. _____

2 Saving money to gain interest. _____

3 Act of hiding something. _____

4 Giving up weapons. _____

5 Putting off to a later time. _____

6 A number or quantity to make complete. _____

7 A situation of mis-rule. _____

8 Opposite of something which is exaggerated. _____

Suffix ence

The suffix ence has come to us from French and indicates an
ABSTRACT NOUN. There is often a related **ADJECTIVE** ending in 'ent'.

	ADJECTIVE	**NOUN**
e.g.	conveni**ent**	conveni**ence**
	sil**ent**	sil**ence**

Below are 5 NOUNS ending in ence. Write sentences for each one.

patience   intelligence   defence   evidence   influence

_____

_____

_____

_____

_____

_____

_____

_____

_____

_____

In the box below are 8 less common NOUNS ending in ence.
Match each one to the correct meaning.

persistence	impudence	turbulence	consequence
deterrence	competence	affluence	subsidence

1   Ability to do something well.   _____

2   Cheekiness or rudeness.   _____

3   Result.   _____

4   Movement or upset due to storminess or violence.   _____

5   Wealth.   _____

6   Sinking into the ground (e.g., building).   _____

7   Method or means to prevent or discourage
    (e.g. crime, war).   _____

8   When you continue firmly or obstinately in doing
    something.   _____

Suffix ance

The suffix has the same sound as ence and is used in the same way.

Some common words ending in ance are shown below.

performance   brilliance   romance   appearance
insurance   allowance   attendance   instance
distance   importance

Match the meanings on the left with the ance words on the right.

a) Unwillingness.   ignorance

b) Similarity in appearance.   circumstance

c) Meaning, importance.   grievance

d) Lack of knowledge.   resemblance

e) Situation, external condition.   fragrance

f) Something that is annoying.   arrogance

g) Ability to put up with trouble, pain etc. significance

h) Sweet smell, perfume.   reluctance

i) Reason to complain.   endurance

j) Pride, conceit.   nuisance

Choose ence or ance to complete the words below.
(Use a dictionary if you are not sure of the meaning.)

1 assist_____
2 persever_____
3 occurr_____
4 experi_____
5 reassur_____
6 eleg_____
7 extravag_____

8 conveni_____
9 obedi_____
10 depend_____
11 avoid_____
12 coincid_____
13 reluct_____
14 accept_____

15 resid_____
16 resist_____
17 insist_____
18 audi_____
19 neglig_____
20 mainten_____

Suffix cy

> This suffix also denotes an **ABSTRACT NOUN**, and words with this ending have come from French and Latin. Many of these words end in 'ncy'. There is often a related **ADJECTIVE**.
>
> | | **ADJECTIVE** | **NOUN** |
> |---|---|---|
> | e.g. | urg<u>ent</u> | urg<u>ency</u> |
> | | expect<u>ant</u> | expect<u>ancy</u> |
> | | obstin<u>ate</u> | obstin<u>acy</u> |

Read the cy words below. Then use one to complete the sentences.

deficiency   infancy   secrecy   currency   redundancy
emergency   bankruptcy   pregnancy   conspiracy   literacy

1   During the early part of her _____ the woman felt very unwell.

2   If you go abroad you need foreign _____.

3   When he reached the age of 60, the man accepted voluntary _____.

4   A _____ in important vitamins and minerals can lead to serious health problems.

5   After the collapse of his business, the man faced _____.

6   During _____ a child's brain develops very rapidly.

7   If you can read and write well, you have a good _____ level.

8   A burst appendix is usually treated as an _____.

9   A _____ is a plot which is planned in _____.

Make NOUNS ending in cy from the ADJECTIVES below.

ADJECTIVE	NOUN	ADJECTIVE	NOUN
1 dependent	_____	7 delicate	_____
2 recent	_____	8 decent	_____
3 private	_____	9 vacant	_____
4 fluent	_____	10 supreme	_____
5 lenient	_____	11 frequent	_____
6 aristocratic	_____	12 diplomatic	_____

Suffix ism

This suffix denotes an <u>ABSTRACT NOUN</u> signifying a condition, idea, quality or system of belief.

e.g. Commun<u>ism</u>, Catholic<u>ism</u>, feudal<u>ism</u>, real<u>ism</u>.

The suffix ism is from Greek.

QUIZ

Answer the following questions which require you to understand the meaning of various ism words.

1 What advantage do people have if they are brought up in an environment of bilingual<u>ism</u>?

_____

2 Is China's economic system based on commun<u>ism</u> or capital<u>ism</u>? _____

3 Name a country where Buddh<u>ism</u> is the main religion. _____

4 If you are arrested for terror<u>ism</u>, what crime might you have committed and for what reason?

_____

5 In what situation might somebody become a victim of age<u>ism</u>?

_____

6 If something is an anachron<u>ism</u>, is it out-of-date or very modern? _____

7 Is Impression<u>ism</u> a style relating to Art, Music or Literature? _____

8 What is the opposite of alcohol<u>ism</u>?
   a) pauper<u>ism</u>   b) reduction<u>ism</u>   c) teetotal<u>ism</u> _____

9 Is altru<u>ism</u> a positive or negative quality? _____

10 If you show antagon<u>ism</u> towards somebody, would you like or dislike them? _____

11 What is the opposite of optim<u>ism</u>? _____

12 If you agree with pacif<u>ism</u>, what would you be opposed to? _____

13 What people have Juda<u>ism</u> as their religion? _____

14 If a leader is accused of despot<u>ism</u>, will he or she be popular or unpopular? _____

15 Is patriot<u>ism</u>   a) a love of oneself,   b) a love of animals
                        c) a love of one's country? _____

Suffix age

> The suffix age indicates an **ABSTRACT NOUN** and it has come to us from French. It is pronounced /ij/.
>
> e.g. postage, leakage, advantage.

Can you think of a word ending in age to match the meanings below?

1   A home for children with no parents.   _ _ _ _ _ _ age
2   Deliberate damage of machinery, etc.   _ _ _ _ _ age
3   A drink (e.g., tea, coffee etc.).   _ _ _ _ _ age
4   House attached to a church.   _ _ _ _ _ age
5   Not enough of something.   _ _ _ _ _ age
6   Long-term loan for a property.   _ _ _ _ _ age
7   Spying.   _ _ _ _ _ _ age
8   Something small wrapped up in paper.   _ _ _ _ age
9   A fraction out of a hundred.   _ _ _ _ _ _ _ age
10 A drawback.   _ _ _ _ _ _ _ _ _ age
11 You will see this after a bomb goes off.   _ _ _ _ _ age
12 Wedding ceremony.   _ _ _ _ _ age
13 Bravery.   _ _ _ _ age
14 Feathers covering a bird.   _ _ _ _ age
15 Journey to a religious shrine.   _ _ _ _ _ _ age

Look up the words below in a dictionary and write your own sentences for them.

carnage   camouflage   umbrage   dotage

_____

_____

_____

_____

_____

_____

Suffix ure and tude

The suffixes ure and tude are 2 further suffixes denoting an **ABSTRACT NOUN** which have come to us from French.

The suffix ure is almost always preceded by 't' or 's'. e.g. mixture, measure.

The suffix tude is always preceded by 'i'. e.g. gratitude

s	c	u	l	p	t	u	r	e	m
t	a	f	i	x	t	u	r	e	o
r	r	u	p	t	u	r	e	x	i
u	i	t	w	e	u	d	l	p	s
c	c	u	l	t	u	r	e	o	t
t	a	r	v	c	b	p	r	s	u
u	t	e	x	t	u	r	e	u	r
r	u	f	r	a	c	t	u	r	e
e	r	a	s	u	r	e	j	e	i
f	e	a	t	u	r	e	y	s	x

Find 13 ure words in the word-square.

(Words go ACROSS and DOWN only.)

c _ _ _ _ _ _ ure   f _ _ ure

c _ _ _ ure   m _ _ _ _ ure

e _ _ _ ure   r _ _ _ ure

e _ _ _ _ ure   s _ _ _ _ _ _ ure

f _ _ _ ure   s _ _ _ _ _ ure

f _ _ _ ure   t _ _ _ ure

f _ _ _ _ ure

Fill in the missing vowels in the ure words below and learn the spellings.

1   m _ n _ _ t _ r _   6   _ rch _ t _ ct _ r _

2   _ xp _ nd _ t _ r _   7   l _ t _ r _ t _ r _

3   t _ mp _ r _ t _ r _   8   m _ n _ f _ ct _ r _

4   s _ gn _ t _ r _   9   l _ _ s _ r _

5   f _ rn _ t _ r _   10 s _ _ z _ r _

Check the meaning of the 4 tude words below and use each one to complete the sentences.

> aptitude   fortitude   solitude   multitude

1   A _____ of people came to the concert.

2   He disliked company and spent most of his time in _____.

3   She had no _____ at all for foreign languages.

4   _____ means strength or courage in a difficult situation.

Suffixes hood , ship and dom

The 3 suffixes below are from Old English. They all indicate **ABSTRACT NOUNS.**

The suffix hood is from Old English 'hād' meaning state or nature.

e.g.   child<u>hood</u> = state of being a child.

The suffix ship is from O.E. 'scipe' and indicates a state, position
or specific type of skill.

e.g.   citizen<u>ship</u> = state of being a citizen.
         king<u>ship</u> = position of being a king.
         seaman<u>ship</u> = skill of being a seaman.

The suffix dom is from O.E. 'dōm' meaning judgement. It indicates
a state, condition or position of power over others.

e.g.   bore<u>dom</u> = state of being bored.
         duke<u>dom</u> = territory over which a duke has power.

Choose hood or ship to complete the words below.

1 baby_____	8 neighbour_____	15 champion_____
2 workman_____	9 sponsor_____	16 relation_____
3 leader_____	10 apprentice_____	17 hard_____
4 likeli_____	11 censor_____	18 liveli_____
5 nation_____	12 mother_____	19 saint_____
6 salesman_____	13 woman_____	20 scholar_____
7 librarian_____	14 partner_____	21 priest_____

Unscramble the letters below to make 6 words ending in dom .

(The first letter of number 6 has been underlined to help you.)

1 r a m s d t o   _____

2 s w o i d m   _____

3 m i g o d k n   _____

4 m m r y d a t r o   _____

5 m r o e d f e   _____

6 d f c <u>o</u> a f m i i l o   _____

Suffix er

> There are several suffixes in English to denote 'A person who...'.
>
> The most common one is **er** which is from Old English.
>
> e.g.   clean<u>er</u> = A person who cleans.

Solve the anagrams below to find 12 NOUNS ending in er .

(Your teacher will give you the first letter if you are stuck!)

1   e b r c i l m   _____
2   r l g a b e m   _____
3   p e r r o t e r   _____
4   a r r e w d   _____
5   r i e j l a   _____
6   m g u r g e s l   _____

7   r r s w e e t l   _____
8   r e p e k e   _____
9   k p a e s r e   _____
10   u g r l j g e   _____
11   e n r i p a t   _____
12   a r s e k t   _____

Follow the correct suffixing rule to add er to the base word below.

1   sin   + er = _____
2   day-trip   + er = _____
3   observe   + er = _____
4   toddle   + er = _____
5   train   + er = _____

6   distil   + er = _____
7   buy   + er = _____
8   outfit   + er = _____
9   carry   + er = _____
10   retail   + er = _____

Name the word: What do you call a person who?

1   Goes to live illegally in somebody else's house.   s _ _ _ _ _ er

2   Teaches at college or university.   l _ _ _ _ _ _ er

3   Goes around the world.   g _ _ _ _ _ -t _ _ _ _ _ er

4   Throws people out of night clubs if troublesome.   b _ _ _ _ er

5   Travels to and from a city to work.   c _ _ _ _ _ _ er

6   Makes things out of clay.   p _ _ _ er

7   Is past the age of working.   p _ _ _ _ _ _ _ er

8   Makes false money or documents.   f _ _ _ _ er

9   Introduces T.V. or radio programmes.   p _ _ _ _ _ _ _ er

10   Brings out books.   p _ _ _ _ _ _ _ er

Suffix or

> The suffix **or** is used instead of **er** on some words to denote 'A person who…'. In most cases the **or** ending is preceded by 't'.
>
> e.g. editor, actor.

Find 15 words in the square below which end in or. Match each word to the clues below. *(Words go ACROSS and DOWN only.)*

c	o	m	p	e	t	i	t	o	r	u	f
o	p	d	i	c	t	a	t	o	r	s	a
n	e	e	j	v	a	l	s	e	q	p	t
d	r	c	a	v	i	a	t	o	r	e	r
u	a	o	v	i	s	i	t	o	r	c	a
c	t	r	n	d	e	b	t	o	r	t	n
t	o	a	n	c	e	s	t	o	r	a	s
o	r	t	b	m	i	t	c	p	k	t	l
r	s	o	l	i	c	i	t	o	r	o	a
h	t	r	a	i	t	o	r	u	g	r	t
b	e	n	e	f	a	c	t	o	r	m	o
d	o	p	r	o	p	r	i	e	t	o	r

1 This person owes money.   _ _ _ _ _ _

2 This person helps you find telephone numbers.   _ _ _ _ _ _ _ _

3 This person betrays his/her country.   _ _ _ _ _ _ _

4 This person is the owner (e.g., property, business).   _ _ _ _ _ _ _ _ _ _

5 This person is good at languages.   _ _ _ _ _ _ _ _ _

6 This person was in your family a long time ago.   _ _ _ _ _ _ _ _

7 This person gives money to good causes or to individuals in need.   _ _ _ _ _ _ _ _ _

8 This person likes flying.   _ _ _ _ _ _

9 This person takes part in a sports contest.   _ _ _ _ _ _ _ _ _ _

10 This person paints your house.   _ _ _ _ _ _ _ _

11 This person works on a bus or in a concert hall.   _ _ _ _ _ _ _ _ _

12 This person is a legal expert.   _ _ _ _ _ _ _ _ _

13 This person watches a sports event.   _ _ _ _ _ _ _ _

14 This person may drop in and see you.   _ _ _ _ _ _ _

15 This person rules with absolute power.   _ _ _ _ _ _ _ _

Suffix ist

The suffix ist is another ending used for people.

It comes from the Greek language, and indicates somebody who follows a certain belief system, somebody who practises an art, trade or profession, or somebody who has specialist subject knowledge.

e.g. Buddhist, pianist, herbalist, economist.

Read the ist words below. Then put them in the correct category.

sociologist   cellist   psychologist   receptionist
telephonist   trombonist   chiropodist   florist   geologist
harpist   novelist   typist   physicist   vocalist   pharmacist
zoologist   flautist   cardiologist   pianist   biologist
dentist   journalist   botanist   psychiatrist   radiologist
tobacconist   anaesthetist   violinist

Health Practitioner	Musician	Subject Specialist	Job (Not health care)

Quiz: 'Call My Bluff'

1 Is a **'taxidermist'** somebody who — a) repairs taxis   b) stuffs animals c) collects taxes?

2 Is a **'sinologist'** somebody who — a) studies Chinese language and culture b) has sinus problems   c) paints signs?

3 Is a **'campanologist'** somebody who — a) rings bells   b) repairs clocks c) studies military campaigns?

4 Is a **'bigamist'** somebody who — a) hates women   b) studies butterflies c) has two wives?

5 Is a **'philanthropist'** somebody who — a) studies philosophy   b) hates mankind c) does good works?

6 Is a **'seismologist'** somebody who studies — a) earthquakes   b) marine life c) ancient civilisations?

Suffix $\boxed{\text{an}}$

> **Another ending denoting a person is $\boxed{\text{an}}$ which can take several forms.** e.g. milk<u>man</u>, libra<u>rian</u>, magi<u>cian</u>, Mexi<u>can</u>, etc.
>
> **It is used mostly for nationalities and jobs.**

Complete the nationalities below by putting in the missing vowels.

1 _ r _ b _ _ n

2 N _ rw _ g _ _ _

3 _ _ str _ _ _

4 V _ n _ z _ _ lan

5 B _ lg _ _ _

6 R _ m _ n _ _ n

7 C _ n _ d _ _ n

8 S _ r _ _ n

9 _ r _ n _ _ n

10 T _ b _ t _ _

11 K _ r _ _ n

12 P _ r _ v _ _ n

> **Words ending in $\boxed{\text{cian}}$ have come from a root word ending in 'ic' + suffix 'man'.** e.g. mag<u>ic</u> + <u>man</u> = mag<u>ician</u>

What $\boxed{\text{cian}}$ word means?

1 Somebody who prescribes glasses or lenses.   o _ _ _ _ _ _ _ _

2 Somebody who recommends special diets for those
who have health problems.   d _ _ _ _ _ _ _ _ _

3 A medical doctor.   ph _ _ _ _ _ _ _

4 Somebody who is expert at Maths.   m _ _ _ _ _ _ _ _ _ _ _ _

5 Somebody in government.   p _ _ _ _ _ _ _ _ _

6 Somebody who knows about machines and technology. t _ _ _ _ _ _ _ _ _

7 This person will help you if your lights fuse.   e _ _ _ _ _ _ _ _ _ _

8 Somebody who can improve your looks with
cosmetics, etc.   b _ _ _ _ _ _ _ _

Unscramble the words below which all end in $\boxed{\text{man}}$.

(The first letter has been underlined to help you.)

1 a m <u>s</u> o n w n   _____

2 a c <u>p</u> i o e l m n   _____

3 n m t a h a c <u>w</u>   _____

4 o s m <u>s</u> e a p n k _____

5 e <u>f</u> m o n r a   _____

6 e <u>n</u> l m a o n b   _____

7 n r a <u>f</u> m i e   _____

8 n a <u>s</u> l e a s m   _____

9 n a m <u>c</u> r a i h   _____

10 a e t <u>s</u> t m a n s _____

Suffixes ess , ling and ee

> The suffixes ess , ling and ee are 3 more **NOUN** suffixes denoting people.
>
> The suffix ess is from French and denotes the feminine form of a related word.
> e.g. princ<u>ess</u>, actr<u>ess</u>.
>
> The suffix ling is from Old English and expresses the idea of something small.
> **It is not very common.**
> e.g. dar<u>ling</u> (from O.E. 'dēor' = deer)
>
> The suffix ee is from French and indicates a person affected by some action,
> performing some action or in a particular situation.
> e.g. evacu<u>ee</u>, absent<u>ee</u>, refer<u>ee</u>.

Write the word ending in ess to match the meanings below.

1 This person has invited you to her house for a party, dinner, etc.   h _ _ _ _ _ _ _

2 A female deity.   g _ _ _ _ _ _

3 This person is in charge of a shop or business.   m _ _ _ _ _ _ _ _

4 This person has killed somebody.   m _ _ _ _ _ _ _

5 This person will inherit land or property.   h _ _ _ _ _ _

6 A female tiger.   t _ _ _ _ _ _

7 This woman is the owner of a shop or business.   p _ _ _ _ _ _ _ _ _ _ _

8 The wife of a duke.   d _ _ _ _ _ _

9 Her husband is head of the town council.   m _ _ _ _ _ _ _

10 This woman runs a school.   h _ _ _ _ _ _ _ _ _

11 The wife of an emperor.   e _ _ _ _ _ _

12 This woman collects bus fares.   c _ _ _ _ _ _ _ _ _ _

Choose ling or ee to complete the words below.

1 earth_____   6 trust_____   11 detain_____

2 gos_____   7 fledge_____   12 seed_____

3 address_____   8 weak_____   13 amput_____

4 pay_____   9 divorc_____   14 escap_____

5 refug_____   10 employ_____   15 sib_____

Noun Revision Sheet: Abstract Nouns

Apply your suffixing rules to the word-sums below to make 16 ABSTRACT NOUNS.
You will have to DOUBLE, DROP 'e', CHANGE 'y' to 'i' or JUST ADD the suffix.

1 entitle + ment = _____

2 store + age = _____

3 jolly + ity = _____

4 hero + ism = _____

5 excel + ence = _____

6 prefer + ence = _____

7 sinful + ness = _____

8 employ + ment = _____

9 likely + hood = _____

10 rely + ance = _____

11 weary + ness = _____

12 stop + age = _____

13 sane + ity = _____

14 escape + ism = _____

15 annoy + ance = _____

16 merry + ment = _____

Choose **tion** or **sion** to complete the words below.

1 inscrip_____

2 renova_____

3 exclu_____

4 adop_____

5 man_____

6 inten_____

7 promo_____

8 comprehen_____

9 exten_____

10 disrup_____

11 suspen_____

12 excur_____

Choose **ness** or **ity** to complete the words below.

(Remember your suffixing rules.)

1 active + _____ = _____

2 lonely + _____ = _____

3 stupid + _____ = _____

4 cheerful + _____ = _____

5 silly + _____ = _____

6 public + _____ = _____

7 humid + _____ = _____

8 captive + _____ = _____

9 sincere + _____ = _____

10 nude + _____ = _____

Choose **ence** or **ance** to complete the words below.

1 exist_____

2 reluct_____

3 ignor_____

4 confid_____

5 magnific_____

6 coincid_____

7 inherit_____

8 innoc_____

9 perform_____

10 resembl_____

11 repent_____

12 insist_____

Noun Practice Sheet

Apply your suffixing rules to the word-sums below to make 16 ABSTRACT NOUNS.
You will have to DOUBLE, DROP 'e', CHANGE 'y' to 'i' or JUST ADD the suffix.

1 seep   +   age = _____   9 betray   +   al = _____

2 defy   + ance = _____   10 lively   + hood = _____

3 deter   +   ent = _____   11 refine   + ment = _____

4 refer   + ence = _____   12 ugly   + ness = _____

5 human +   ity = _____   13 admit   + ance = _____

6 slip   +   age = _____   14 enjoy   + ment = _____

7 subside + ence = _____   15 enclose +   ure = _____

8 symbol +   ism = _____   16 bore   +   dom = _____

Choose | or | or | er | to complete the words below.

1 foreign____   5 inspect____   9 sculpt____

2 photograph____   6 solicit____   10 may____

3 narrat____   7 employ____   11 present____

4 prison____   8 retail____   12 propriet____

All the suffixes below are used to denote a person.
Choose the correct suffix to complete the words below.

ist   ian   ee   ess   or   er

1 music_____   8 histor_____   15 sail_____

2 trust_____   9 Iran_____   16 credit_____

3 refer_____   10 manager_____   17 comed_____

4 operat_____   11 violin_____   18 absent_____

5 botan_____   12 design_____   19 direct_____

6 priest_____   13 host_____   20 entertain_____

7 reception_____   14 final_____   21 jur_____

Noun Practice Sheet

**<u>Use your suffixing to do the word-sums below. You will have to
DOUBLE, DROP 'e', CHANGE 'y' to 'i' or JUST ADD the suffix.</u>**

1 commit + ment = _____   9 grieve + ance = _____

2 enforce + ment = _____   10 convey + ance = _____

3 punctual + ity = _____   11 conceal + ment = _____

4 expose + ure = _____   12 immense + ity = _____

5 race + ism = _____   13 kin + ship = _____

6 false + hood = _____   14 waste + age = _____

7 plain + ness = _____   15 pretty + ness = _____

8 merry + ment = _____   16 acquit + al = _____

**<u>Choose the correct suffix from those below to make
20 ABSTRACT NOUNS.</u>**

*(You might have to DROP the 'e' of the base word if adding a VOWEL suffix,
or CHANGE 'y' to 'i' if the base word ends in 'y'.)*

ness   ity   hood   ment   ship   ism

1 owner_____   8 mother_____   15 partner_____

2 hero_____   9 formal_____   16 widow_____

3 empty_____   10 nervous_____   17 resent_____

4 priest_____   11 barren_____   18 bitter_____

5 settle_____   12 improve_____   19 severe_____

6 humid_____   13 punish_____   20 mobile_____

7 critic_____   14 tour_____

Verb suffixes for tense: s , ing and ed

> **The 3 most common VERB suffixes are s , ing and ed .**
> **They are used to mark TENSE.**
> **These endings are sometimes called PARTICIPLES.**

Choose s , ing or ed to complete the words below.

1 He walk____ for hours before he reach____ his destination.

2 Water boil____ at 100°C.

3 The wind was howl____ and the rain was lash____ down as the boys attempt____ to put up their tents.

4 He usually get____ up at 6.30 a.m. on working days, but at weekends he like____ to have a lie-in.

5 "Look at that man – he's try____ to break into that car."

6 A skunk give____ off an evil smell to defend itself.

7 They wait____ for half an hour, but the bus fail____ to turn up.

8 "I'm go____ to London for a few days next week – can you look after my cats while I'm away?"

9 My parents always listen to classical music, but my grandmother like____ rock and pop!

Questions

1 Which suffix or suffixes is/are associated with the present tense (s)? _____

2 Which suffix is associated with the past tense? Do all the verbs in the past tense need this suffix? _____

3 Which suffix can only be used if the subject is third person singular (i.e., 'he', 'she', 'it', my friend, the man, etc.?) _____

4 Which sentences describe a general statement (i.e., something which is always true)? What tense is used for these sentences?

_____

5 What other sentences use the same tense? What is the normal function of this tense?

_____

6 Which suffix is put on verbs to express the idea of an action or event continuing for some time? _____

7 Which suffix would you expect to find most often in a story? _____

8 Which suffix would you hear in a sports commentary? _____

Suffix en

The suffix en is an Old English verb ending meaning 'to make' or 'to become'.

e.g. to damp<u>en</u> = to make damp
to weak<u>en</u> = to make weak.

It is also used as a <u>PAST PARTICIPLE</u> in irregular verbs.

e.g. write   wrote   writt<u>en</u>

In this form, the past participle often functions as an <u>ADJECTIVE</u>.

ADJECTIVE NOUN

e.g. People have a lot of respect for the <u>written</u> word.

Write the VERB ending in suffix en to complete the sentences below.

1 "You will d_____ me with that loud music."

2 I was very s_____ed to hear that the old lady had died.

3 The egg whites began to s_____ after whisking for a few minutes.

4 We were told to s_____ our pencils before drawing the diagram.

5 We were instructed to f_____ our seat-belts before take-off.

6 The gang leader thr_____ed us with a knife.

7 I decided to fr_____ up with a shower before going out.

8 Reading widely can br_____ your mind.

9 As a child I was always told to str_____ up and stop slouching!

10 The foundations of the building were str_____ed with reinforced concrete.

Write the PAST PARTICIPLE of the VERBS below. Then match each to the NOUNS on the right as in the example.

VERB	PAST PARTICIPLE	NOUN	VERB	PAST PARTICIPLE	NOUN
break	*broken*	lake	steal	_____	cloth
fall	_____	head	swell	_____	lava
freeze	_____	chair	weave	_____	car
rot	_____	tree	melt	_____	ship
shave	_____	apple	sink	_____	ankle

Suffix ate

> The suffix ate is the most common **VERB** suffix from Latin.
> There is often a related **NOUN** ending in tion .
>
> | | **VERB** | **NOUN** |
> | --- | --- | --- |
> | e.g. | regulate | regulation |

Unscramble the letters below to find 10 two-syllable words ending in ate to match the meanings.

1 e t c e r a _____ To make something

2 e c o l a t _____ To find the position of something

3 a r e m e t c _____ To burn a dead body.

4 e r n a a r t _____ To tell a story.

5 e t d b e a _____ To discuss an issue.

6 t o a e r t _____ To go around an axis or centre.

7 q e t e a u _____ To treat as the same as something else.

8 e o d t n a _____ To give money to charity.

9 e t a s a t g n _____ To stand or remain still, to go stale.

10 b e v a i r t _____ To cause to move to and fro, to shake, pulsate.

Choose a 3-syllable word ending in ate to complete the sentences below. The first letter has been given to help you.

1 Christmas is a time to c _ _ _ _ _ ate.

2 Some animals h _ _ _ _ _ ate in winter.

3 Babies like to i _ _ _ ate their parents by watching their faces.

4 Blood c _ _ _ _ _ ates round the body.

5 On the training course we had to d _ _ _ _ _ _ _ ate leadership ability.

6 It was hard to e _ _ _ _ ate how old the man was.

7 Some sailors can n _ _ _ _ ate without using a compass.

8 During the potato famine in Ireland, many people were forced to e _ _ _ _ ate to America.

9 Some parents prefer to e _ _ _ ate their children at home rather than sending them to school.

10 Many children like to d _ _ _ _ ate the Christmas tree.

Suffix ate

Choose a 4-syllable word ending in ate to complete the sentences below.

(The first letter has been given to help you.)

1 The workers had to e _ _ _ _ ate the building when the fire alarm went off.

2 John F. Kennedy was not the first American president to be
   a _ _ _ _ _ _ _ ated.

3 The whole city was d _ _ _ _ _ ated by the earthquake.

4 A memorial was erected to c _ _ _ _ _ _ _ ate those who died in the war.

5 The caravan could easily a _ _ _ _ _ _ _ ate six people.

6 The girl received may cards to c _ _ _ _ _ _ _ _ ate her on her outstanding
   examination results.

7 If you e _ _ _ _ _ _ ate, you say that something is much worse or much bigger
   than it really is.

8 They boy was not allowed to p _ _ _ _ _ _ _ ate in the swimming competition
   because he was too young.

9 Some people a _ _ _ _ _ _ ate a lot of junk because they can't bear to throw
   anything away.

10 Drugs like aspirin are given to a _ _ _ _ _ ate pain.

11 When detectives i _ _ _ _ _ _ _ ate a crime such as murder or robbery, they
    often have to i _ _ _ _ _ _ _ ate suspects.

**Put the syllables in order in order to make 4 or 5-syllable words ending
in ate. Then match each one to the correct meaning.**

a) nav gate cir i cum _____   To put off doing something.

b) ō en tate dis ri   _____   To poison with chemicals.

c) ate cras tin prō   _____   To pretend to be somebody else.

d) cate in i tox   _____   To wipe out.

e) er ō ate blit   _____   To sail around the world.

f) ate con in tam   _____   To guess a number that is too low.

g) es ate un tim der   _____   To make somebody confused
                                          about direction.

h) per ate son im   _____   To make drunk.

Suffix ify

The suffix ify is another Latinate verb suffix which has come into English through French. It means 'to make'. There is often a related <u>ADJECTIVE</u>.

	<u>ADJECTIVE</u>	<u>VERB</u>
e.g.	solid	solid<u>ify</u> (= to make solid)

Read the words which end in ify .and match each to the meaning.

deify   simplify   unify   fortify   modify

sanctify   clarify   terrify   purify   magnify

1 To make easier. _____

2 To make clear. _____

3 To make one. _____

4 To make afraid. _____

5 To make into a god. _____

6 To make clean. _____

7 To make stronger. _____

8 To make bigger. _____

9 To make holy. _____

10 To make changes to. _____

Solve the anagrams below to make words ending in ify to match the

meanings below. *(The first letter has been underlined to help you.)*

1 <u>t</u> e i f t s y   To give evidence. _____

2 y f <u>s</u> c p e i   To mention definitely or describe in detail. _____

3 l s y a i f <u>c</u> s   To categorise. _____

4 a i y f c <u>p</u>   To calm, appease. _____

5 r y e <u>v</u> f i   To establish the truth. _____

6 y c <u>r</u> i e t f   To put right. _____

Now use each word to complete the sentences below.

1 He tried his best to _____ his mistakes.

2 In the Biology test we had to _____ various plants.

3 Before accusing somebody, you should _____ the facts.

4 The trial collapsed because a key witness refused to _____.

5 It is not always the best policy to _____ the enemy.

6 The instructions did not _____ what had to be done first.

Suffix ise

The suffix ise is a common **VERB** suffix which came originally from the Greek word 'izein'. Then it entered Latin and was changed to 'izare'. The French changed it to 'iser' and it finally entered English as ize or ise.

In Britain the ise spelling seems to be replacing the former ize spelling but most words can be spelt with either suffix. In American English the ize spelling is used.

The ise suffix is put on **ADJECTIVES** or **NOUNS** to make them **VERBS**.

e.g. public   (Adjective) ⟶ public<u>ise</u>
apology (Noun)   ⟶ apolog<u>ise</u>

Fill in the missing letters to make 12 words ending in ise to match the meanings below.

1	r _ _ _ g _ ise	To know somebody or something on sight.
2	t _ _ r _ _ ise	To inspire great fear in somebody.
3	v _ _ d _ _ ise	To cause deliberate damage to property.
4	m _ _ o _ ise	To learn by heart.
5	e _ p _ _ _ ise	To lay stress on.
6	m _ d _ _ _ ise	To make up-to-date.
7	s _ p _ r _ ise	To oversee workers.
8	p _ _ l _ _ ise	To make known by newspaper or television.
9	l _ g _ _ ise	To make lawful.
10	h _ p _ o _ ise	To put somebody into a trance.
11	s _ m _ _ _ _ ise	To feel sorry for somebody in misfortune.
12	c _ _ t _ _ ise	To find fault with somebody or something.

Choose 4 of the words below and write your own sentences.

advertise   apologise   hospitalise   liquidise   specialise
organise   realise   subsidise   utilise

_____

_____

_____

_____

Suffix ise

Use a dictionary to match the ise words below to the dictionary definitions. Try and learn the spellings.

jeopardise   synchronise   scrutinise   compromise   idolise

immobilise   monopolise   ostracise   tyrannise   galvanise

1   To place in a situation of danger or loss. _____

2   To exclude from society, refuse to associate with. _____

3   To settle a dispute by making a concession. _____

4   To take sole possession or control of something. _____

5   To keep time with, go at the same pace as. _____

6   To render something or somebody unable to move. _____

7   To rule despotically or cruelly over. _____

8   To examine something very carefully. _____

9   To stimulate or rouse into action. _____

10 To worship like a god. _____

Now use each word to complete the sentences below.

1   The man _____d the contract very carefully before he signed it.

2   The soldiers _____d their watches before beginning the operation.

3   The leader who _____d his people for many years was eventually overthrown in a military coup.

4   Some children _____ others by refusing to let them join in play or other activities.

5   He _____d his chances of going to university by failing all his A-Levels.

6   Young children often _____ their parent's attention.

7   The sight of the finishing line _____d the athlete into a final spurt of effort.

8   The plan was to _____ the enemy's tanks in the air campaigns before beginning the ground attack.

9   Many pop stars are _____d by their fans.

10 Each side defended its own principles, but in the end both sides had to _____ in order to reach an agreement.

Verb Practice Sheet

Do the word-sums below by adding the VERB suffixes to the base words. Remember to apply your suffixing rules.

1 final   + ise = _____

2 expel   + ed = _____

3 captive + ate = _____

4 deny   + ed = _____

5 refer   + ing = _____

6 ideal   + ise = _____

7 moisture + ise = _____

8 conceal + ed = _____

9 hurry   + ing = _____

10 simplify + ed = _____

11 instil   + ed = _____

12 private + ise = _____

13 legal   + ise = _____

14 carry   + ed = _____

15 type   + ify = _____

16 vaccine + ate = _____

Choose **ify** , **ise** or **ate** **to add to the VERB stems below.**

1 sign_____

2 familiar_____

3 loc_____

4 navig_____

5 steril_____

6 gener_____

7 class_____

8 pollin_____

9 vac_____

10 item_____

11 fossil_____

12 terr_____

13 intoxic_____

14 victim_____

15 brutal_____

16 fort_____

17 qual_____

18 illumin_____

Make verbs ending in **ify** , **ise** or **ate** **from the ADJECTIVES below.**

ADJECTIVE	VERB	ADJECTIVE	VERB
1 natural	_____	9 public	_____
2 solid	_____	10 false	_____
3 pure	_____	11 co-operative	_____
4 modern	_____	12 scandalous	_____
5 intense	_____	13 equal	_____
6 domestic	_____	14 fertile	_____
7 active	_____	15 glorious	_____
8 mobile	_____	16 original	_____

Suffixes ing and ed as ADJECTIVE Endings

The suffixes ing and ed are normally VERB endings to denote TENSE.

e.g.   He's stand<u>ing</u> over there.   **(PRESENT Tense)**
She rush<u>ed</u> out of the house. **(PAST Tense)**

But ed and ing become ADJECTIVE suffixes when added to VERBS which are placed directly before a NOUN.

<u>ADJECTIVE</u> <u>NOUN</u>
e.g.   The sleep<u>ing</u> dog growled softly.
The bur<u>ied</u> treasure was never found.

Think of an ADJECTIVE ending in ing to complete the sentences below.

1   The mother picked up the _____ child and hugged him.

2   The police stopped the _____ motorist doing over 100 m.p.h.

3   The _____weather caused many pipes to burst.

4   We looked for shade to escape the _____ sun.

5   The farmer narrowly escaped being gored by the _____ bull.

6   Moths and other _____ insects are attracted to lights.

7   The _____ fans went wild when the final goal was scored.

8   The whole family was gathered round the bed of the _____ woman.

Think of an ADJECTIVE ending in ed to complete the sentences below.

1   We were advised to drink only _____ water.

2   The freshly _____ room looked bright and cheerful.

3   The smell of newly _____ bread is mouth-watering.

4   The panda is an _____ species.

5   Fallen leaves soon become dry and _____.

6   The _____ puppy was in a pitiful state.

7   Pensions are given to _____ people over the age of 60.

8   For lunch we had _____ potatoes with _____ eggs.

Suffixes ing and ed as Adjectives of Feeling

Both ing and ed suffixes are added to certain <u>VERBS</u> to turn them into <u>ADJECTIVES</u> of feeling.

The ing suffix is used to describe events, actions or things, while the ed suffix is used with people.

e.g.   The bor<u>ing</u> film lasted 3 hours.
The children were soon bor<u>ed</u> by the film.

<u>Unscramble the words below to find 8 ADJECTIVES of feeling ending in ed to match the situations.</u>

<u>How would you feel if?</u>

1	e t c i e x d	_____	You're about to go to Disneyland.
2	d g d t i s s u e	_____	You see a slug in the salad.
3	a z a e m d	_____	You've won the lottery.
4	n o a y n e d	_____	The phone keeps ringing while you're trying to work.
5	e a s u r f t r t d	_____	You can't get the last crossword clue.
6	d i o r w e r	_____	You've lost your wallet.
7	d l h i t r l e	_____	You've passed all your GCSEs with top grades.
8	d s a r a s e b m r e	_____	You start singing at the wrong time at the school concert.

<u>Choose a suitable ADJECTIVE ending in ing to complete the sentences below.</u>

1   The film was so _____ that it gave me nightmares.

2   It is _____ to learn how people lived in the past.

3   The instructions for the sponsored walk were so _____ that everybody got lost.

4   The clowns were very _____, but the most _____ act was performed by the trapeze artists.

5   The man found it _____ to be beaten at chess by a 9 year-old boy.

6   Last winter we had a _____ experience when we got trapped in a cable car for more than an hour on a skiing trip.

Suffix $\boxed{y}$

Suffix $\boxed{y}$ is one of the most common **ADJECTIVE** suffixes. It comes from Old English, and is added to **NOUNS** to turn them into **ADJECTIVES**.

	NOUN		**ADJECTIVE**
e.g.	sleep + y	=	sleepy
	rain + y	=	rainy

Can you think of an ADJECTIVE ending in suffix $\boxed{y}$ to complement the NOUNS below?

1 _____ socks

2 _____ weather

3 _____ day

4 _____ orange

5 _____ car

6 _____ food

7 _____ rabbit

8 _____ joke

9 _____ beach

10 _____ hair

11 _____ drink

12 _____ boots

As $\boxed{y}$ is a **VOWEL** suffix, you might have to follow the **DOUBLE** or **DROP 'e'** rule when adding the suffix to the base word.

e.g. skin + y = ski<u>nn</u>y (**DOUBLE**)
shine + y = shiny (**DROP 'e'**)

Unscramble the words below which are all base words to which $\boxed{y}$ can be added. Then add the suffix by following the correct rule.

1 p s t o   _____ + y = _____

2 u t r s   _____ + y = _____

3 t i g r   _____ + y = _____

4 e i s k p   _____ + y = _____

5 l o f p   _____ + y = _____

6 n e t s o   _____ + y = _____

7 l t s a   _____ + y = _____

8 t c a h   _____ + y = _____

9 e i s l m   _____ + y = _____

10 t i c h   _____ + y = _____

11 m l o o g   _____ + y = _____

12 u t l g i   _____ + y = _____

Suffixes ┃ful┃ and ┃less┃

> The suffixes ┃ful┃ and ┃less┃ are from Old English and mean 'full of' and 'without'. They turn **NOUNS** or **VERBS** into **ADJECTIVES**.

Look at the BASE WORDS below and decide if:

1 The **BASE WORD** can take suffix ┃ful┃ only.   e.g. hate**ful**

2 The **BASE WORD** can take suffix ┃less┃ only.   e.g. fault**less**

3 The **BASE WORD** can take both ┃ful┃ and ┃less┃   e.g. hope**ful**
                                                        or hope**less**

Then write each suffix in the correct list.

> sense   play   thought   <u>hope</u>   change   watch
> shame   regard   <u>hate</u>   dread   odour   colour
> <u>fault</u>   distrust   breath   mercy   cheer   fate

'ful' only	'less' only	'ful' and 'less'
hate	fault	hope
_____	_____	_____
_____	_____	_____
_____	_____	_____
_____	_____	_____
_____	_____	_____

Add ┃ful┃ **or** ┃less┃ **to the base words below. Remember to CHANGE 'y' to 'i' if the base word ends in 'y' preceded by a CONSONANT.** e.g. pit<u>y</u> + ful = pit<u>i</u>ful

1 defence + less = _____   7 tune   + less = _____

2 spot   + less = _____   8 glee   + ful = _____

3 play   + ful = _____   9 joy   + less = _____

4 body   + less = _____   10 fancy   + ful = _____

5 duty   + ful = _____   11 fruit   + ful = _____

6 penny   + less = _____   12 revenge + ful = _____

Suffixes worthy , some , like and ish

The suffixes worthy , some , like and ish are all from Old English and they turn **NOUNS** into **ADJECTIVES**.

They are not very common compared to other **ADJECTIVE** suffixes.

e.g.	trust<u>worthy</u>	= worthy of trust
	fear<u>some</u>	= inspiring fear
	bird<u>like</u>	= like a bird
	yellow<u>wish</u>	= a little bit yellow

Choose worthy , some or like to add to the base words below.

Remember to apply your suffixing rules.

1 adventure + _____ = _____
2 quarrel   + _____ = _____
3 blame   + _____ = _____
4 trouble   + _____ = _____
5 business   + _____ = _____
6 life   + _____ = _____
7 meddle   + _____ = _____
8 road   + _____ = _____
9 hand   + _____ = _____
10 sylph   + _____ = _____

11 sea   + _____ = _____
12 weary   + _____ = _____
13 grue   + _____ = _____
14 praise + _____ = _____
15 lady   + _____ = _____
16 whole   + _____ = _____
17 cumber + _____ = _____
18 war   + _____ = _____
19 worry   + _____ = _____
20 news   + _____ = _____

Find 14 words in the square below which can take suffix ish . Then add ish to each word as in the example, using the correct suffixing rule.

(Words go ACROSS and DOWN only.)

o	a	f	s	n	o	b
s	t	y	l	e	D	a
h	b	l	u	e	a	b
e	o	u	g	u	n	y
e	o	m	u	l	e	f
p	k	P	o	l	e	a
r	e	d	S	c	o	t

1 b <u>a b y</u>   + ish = *babyish*
2 b _ _ _   + ish = _____
3 b _ _ _   + ish = _____
4 D _ _ _   + ish = _____
5 l _ _ _   + ish = _____
6 m _ _ _   + ish = _____
7 o _ _   + ish = _____
8 P _ _ _   + ish = _____
9 r _ _   + ish = _____
10 S _ _ _   + ish = _____
11 s _ _ _ _ + ish = _____
12 s _ _ _   + ish = _____
13 s _ _ _   + ish = _____
14 s _ _ _ _ + ish = _____

Suffix OUS

> The suffix OUS is one of the most common **ADJECTIVE** suffixes in English which has come from Latin and French.
>
> It turns a **NOUN** into an **ADJECTIVE**.
>
> | | **NOUN** | **ADJECTIVE** |
> |---|---|---|
> | e.g. | poison | poisonous |
>
> Many OUS words have an 'i' before the suffix.
>
> e.g. glorious, notorious, etc.

Complete the OUS words to match the definitions.

1 Wanting what others have, jealous   en _ _ous
2 Well-known.   f _ _ ous
3 Funny.   h _ _ _ _ ous
4 Naughty.   m _ s _ h _ _ _ ous
5 Very hungry.   r _ v _ _ ous
6 Very angry.   f _ _ _ ous
7 Kind, not mean.   g _ n _ _ ous
8 Wanting to know about everything and everyone.   c _ r _ ous
9 Can't be explained easily.   m _ s _ _ r _ ous
10 Like a film star!   gl _ _ _ _ ous
11 Careful (e.g., if there's danger).   c _ u _ _ ous
12 Wonderful.   m _ r _ _ _ _ ous
13 Very big.   e _ o _ _ ous
14 Brave.   c _ u _ _ g _ ous
15 Very greedy.   gl _ _ t _ _ ous

Read the 5 OUS words below and check the meanings if necessary.
Use each one to complete the sentences.

industrious   oblivious   carnivorous   monotonous   herbivorous

1 When working on his computer, he was _____ of time passing.

2 An _____ person produces more than a lazy one.

3 A lion is a _____ animal, but many of the animals it kills and eats are _____.

4 The job was so _____ that time really dragged.

Suffix OUS

> **Most words ending in OUS have a related NOUN form.**
>
> | | NOUN | ADJECTIVE |
> |---|---|---|
> | e.g. | mystery | myster<u>ious</u> |
> | | fame | fam<u>ous</u> |

Give the related NOUNS from the ADJECTIVES below ending in OUS.

	ADJECTIVE	NOUN		ADJECTIVE	NOUN
1	miraculous	_____	7	courteous	_____
2	conscious	_____	8	religious	_____
3	generous	_____	9	curious	_____
4	various	_____	10	prestigious	_____
5	envious	_____	11	anxious	_____
6	glamorous	_____	12	treacherous	_____

Give the ADJECTIVE ending in OUS which is related to the NOUNS below. (Be careful with your spelling.)

	NOUN	ADJECTIVE		NOUN	ADJECTIVE
1	prosperity	_____	6	population	_____
2	monotony	_____	7	grief	_____
3	fury	_____	8	victory	_____
4	infamy	_____	9	disaster	_____
5	hilarity	_____	10	vigour	_____

Quiz: Answer the following questions to test your knowledge of some less common OUS words.

1 What kind of vote is a <u>unanimous</u> one? _____

2 Name 2 things which are <u>porous</u>. _____ _____

3 Do you talk sense or nonsense if you are <u>delirious</u>? _____

4 Is a <u>gregarious</u> person likely to have a lot of friends or only a few? _____

5 If somebody is <u>obsequious</u>, do they treat you with a lot of respect, or with no respect? _____

6 Would a <u>garrulous</u> person have a lot to say or only a little? _____

7 If something is <u>superfluous</u>, is it needed or not needed? _____

8 Does a <u>pompous</u> person have a good or bad opinion of himself/herself? _____

Suffix tious and cious

> Some words with the OUS suffix have the sound /sh/ before the ending.
>
> In these words, the /sh/ sound is spelt 'ti' or 'ci'.
>
> e.g. ambi<u>ti</u>ous, deli<u>ci</u>ous, etc.

Read the words below which end in tious. Check the meanings and use each one to complete the sentences below.

conscientious   scrumptious   superstitious   ostentatious
nutritious   flirtatious   surreptitious

1 A _____ student deserves to get good results.

2 An _____ person likes to show off.

3 If a meal tastes delicious and is good for you, it can be described as both _____ and _____.

4 A _____ person will probably not walk under a ladder.

5 If a woman is _____, she will try to attract a man's attention.

6 If you do something in a _____ manner, you do it secretly.

Now do the same with the 5 words below which end in cious.

ferocious   vivacious   malicious   avaricious   voracious

1 We were amazed by the child's _____ appetite.

2 An _____ person is miserly and greedy.

3 The house was guarded by a _____ dog.

4 A vandal does _____ damage to property.

5 The man's wife was beautiful and _____.

Choose tious or cious to complete the words below.

| 1 spa____ | 3 infec____ | 5 gra____ | 7 preten____ | 9 cau____ |
| 2 suspi____ | 4 ficti____ | 6 pre____ | 8 repeti____ | 10 vi____ |

Suffix al

The suffix al is one of the most common **ADJECTIVE** suffixes which has come into English from Latin and French, and means 'belonging to'. It turns a **NOUN** into an **ADJECTIVE**. The base word may be a modern English word of Latin or Greek origin.

e.g. historical (from 'history', originally the Greek word 'histor'.)

Or it may have a Latin stem: e.g. local (from Latin 'locus' = place.)

Give the modern English ADJECTIVE ending in al which has come from the Latin words below.

Latin word + meaning	ADJECTIVE ending in 'al'	Latin word + meaning	ADJECTIVE ending in 'al'
1 **dens, dentis** = tooth	_____	9 **māter** = mother	_____
2 **lex, legis** = law	_____	10 **gradus** = step	_____
3 **fiscus** = basket/purse	_____	11 **annus** = year	_____
4 **rūs, ruris** = countryside	_____	12 **spīna** = thorn	_____
5 **corpus** = body	_____	13 **navis** = ship	_____
6 **fātum** = prediction	_____	14 **vōx, vocis** = voice	_____
7 **fīnis** = end	_____	15 **verbum** = word	_____
8 **initium** = beginning	_____	16 **manus** = hand	_____

Now use 12 of the words you have made with al to complete the sentences below.

1 _____ punishment is now il_____ in schools.

2 The _____ instinct is very strong.

3 He decided to leave the city and look for skilled _____ work in a_____ part of England.

4 She was unable to speak after damaging her _____ cords.

5 The pupil was given a _____ warning.

6 A _____ accident is one which causes death.

7 He suffered serious _____ injuries in the car crash, but made a complete recovery after some _____ setbacks.

8 He had a very good career as a _____ officer.

9 The man cancelled his _____ appointment as his toothache disappeared.

Suffix [al]

Complete the [al] words below to match the definitions.

1	Relating to the outside.	e _ t _ _ _ al
2	Perfect.	i _ _ al
3	On time.	p _ _ c _ _ al
4	Lasting forever, continuous.	p _ r _ _ t _ al
5	Having a useful purpose.	f _ _ c _ _ o _ a _
6	Relating to the nose.	n _ _ al
7	You have a choice.	o _ t _ _ _ al
8	Jolly.	j _ _ ial
9	Now and again.	o _ _ a _ i _ _ _ l
10	Unimportant, concerning details only.	tr _ _ _ al
11	Like a son.	f _ l _ al
12	Describing the Middle Ages.	m _ _ i _ _ al
13	Chief, main.	pr _ n _ _ _ al
14	Found everywhere.	u _ i _ _ r _ al
15	Decorative.	o _ _ a _ _ n _ al

Complete the 12 words below which all end in [al] preceded by [ic].

e.g. electri<u>cal</u>, bibli<u>cal</u>, etc.

1	Relating to the eye.	o _ _ ical
2	Holding very extreme views.	f _ n _ _ ical
3	Not believing something to be true.	sc _ _ _ ical
4	Finding fault with something or somebody.	cr _ _ ical
5	Funny.	c _ _ ical
6	Cost-effective.	e _ o _ _ _ ical
7	Exactly the same.	i _ _ n _ ical
8	Shape of the globe.	s _ _ e _ ical
9	Behaving like a despot.	t _ r _ _ _ ical
10	Concerning somebody's life story.	b _ _ g _ _ p _ ical
11	In order of time.	ch _ _ n _ _ o _ ical
12	Self-centred, big-headed.	e _ _ t _ s _ ical

Suffix tial and cial

Some words with the al suffix have the sound /sh/ before the ending.

In these words, the /sh/ sound is spelt 'ti' or 'ci'.

e.g. initial, special etc.

Read the words below which end in tial. Check the meanings and use each one to complete the sentences below.

crucial   financial   superficial   beneficial   facial   racial

1   If something is _____, it is good for you.

2   _____ prejudice is all too common.

3   Most university students depend on _____ support from their parents.

4   It is _____ to watch the time when doing an examination.

5   He received _____ burns in the fire, but luckily they were only _____ so he was not permanently scarred.

Now do the same for the words below ending in cial.

torrential   partial   essential   potential   confidential

1   The camping trip was ruined by _____ rain.

2   Oxygen is _____ for life.

3   The operation was only a _____ success, necessitating further surgery in the future.

4   The girl had great _____ as an athlete, but she was not prepared to train hard every day.

5   Medical records are strictly _____.

Choose tial or cial to complete the words below.

1 commer_____   4 substan_____   7 preferen_____   10 gla_____

2 presiden_____   5 artifi_____   8 residen_____   11 mar_____

3 spa_____   6 provin_____   9 influen_____   12 judi_____

Suffix able

The suffix able is from French and Latin, and changes a <u>VERB</u> into an
<u>ADJECTIVE</u> meaning 'capable of being'.
e.g.   allow<u>able</u>   = Something that is allowed.
employ<u>able</u> = Able to be employed.

<u>Complete the able words below to match the meanings.</u>

1 You can go near it.   a _ _ r _ _ c _ able
2 You can put up with it.   b _ _ _ able
3 To be wished for.   d _ s _ _ able
4 It lasts a long time.   d _ _ able
5 Easily annoyed.   i _ _ i _ able
6 Prominent, easy to spot.   n _ _ i _ _ able
7 Cheap enough to buy.   a _ _ o _ _ able
8 Able to be carried.   p _ _ _ able
9 You can guess the outcome.   pr _ _ i _ _ able
10 It will definitely happen.   i _ e _ _ table
11 You can't get it back.   i _ r _ tr _ _ _ able
12 Not a sensible course of action.   i _ a _ v _ _ able
13 Unbearable.   i _ s _ f _ _ _ able
14 Amazing.   r _ m _ r _ able
15 Unfriendly, unwelcoming.   i _ h _ s _ _ _ able

<u>Check the meanings of the 5 able words below and use them</u>
<u>in sentences of your own.</u>

laudable   unpalatable   impregnable   viable   amiable

_____
_____
_____
_____
_____
_____

Suffix ible

| The suffix ible has the same function as able and has the same |
| pronunciation, but is less frequent. |
| e.g terr ible , collaps ible . |

Unscramble the words below to make 5 common words ending in ible . There is a clue to help you.

Clue

1   b o r i h e r l   _____   Ugh!

2   s b p i o s l e   _____   Maybe.

3   s n b s i e e l   _____   Good idea.

4   e e l n b i d i   _____   Don't eat it!

5   l e s i v b i   _____   I can see it.

Complete the ible words below to match the meanings.

1   a _ _ ible   Can be heard.

2   e _ _ _ ible   Fit or qualified to be chosen; suitable.

3   f _ _ _ ible   Possible, practicable.

4   f _ _ _ ible   Can be bent; adaptable.

5   g _ _ _ ible   Naive, easily deceived.

6   i _ _ _ _ _ ible Unbelievable.

7   i _ _ _ _ ible   Can't be deleted or erased (e.g., ink).

8   i _ _ _ _ _ ible Can't be conquered.

9   l _ _ ible   Can be read.

10 r _ s _ _ n _ ible Can be trusted.

Choose ible or able to complete the words below.

1 charit_____   5 depend_____   9 fashion_____

2 pay_____   6 prevent_____   10 suscept_____

3 access_____   7 divis_____   11 insepar_____

4 permiss_____   8 plaus_____   12 excit_____

Suffix ent

> The suffix ent is an __ADJECTIVE__ suffix of Latin origin, which has entered English through French. In most cases there is a related __NOUN__ form ending in ence or ency.
>
> | | __ADJECTIVE__ | __NOUN__ |
> |---|---|---|
> | e.g. | confident | confidence |
> | | lenient | leniency |

Join the syllables to make 10 ADJECTIVES ending in ent. Then match each one to the meanings given.

1	ab	parent	_____	a)	Reliant.
2	ad	pendent	_____	b)	Efficient.
3	ap	venient	_____	c)	Often.
4	com	tent	_____	d)	Lasting indefinitely.
5	de	manent	_____	e)	Next to.
6	con	sorbent	absorbent	f)	Powerful.
7	fre	petent	_____	g)	Clear to sight or mind.
8	in	jacent	_____	h)	Like a sponge.
9	per	solent	_____	i)	Rude.
10	po	quent	_____	j)	Suitable, within easy reach.

Use your dictionary to check the meanings of the ent words in the sentences below in order to answer the questions.

1 What situation might make you feel despondent? _____

2 Would you expect a diligent student to get good or bad results? _____

3 What problem would you have if you were insolvent? _____

4 Would a belligerent nation make war or peace? _____

5 Would indulgent parents spoil or be strict with their children? _____

6 When would somebody feel penitent? _____

7 Would a reticent person say a lot about himself or very little? _____

8 Would an indolent person get a lot of work done or only a little? _____

9 If somebody has prominent ears, what would they look like? _____

10 Would you treat an eminent person with respect or scorn? _____

Suffix `ant`

The **ADJECTIVE** ending `ant` is like `ent`. It is pronounced in exactly the same way, but is less common than `ent`. In most cases there is a related **NOUN** ending in `ance` or `ancy`.

	ADJECTIVE	**NOUN**
e.g.	defi<u>ant</u>	defi<u>ance</u>
	const<u>ant</u>	const<u>ancy</u>

Complete the 12 `ant` words below to match the meanings.

1 r _ p _ _ nant   Disgusting.
2 j _ b _ _ ant   Exultant, joyful (e.g., at a victory).
3 fl _ _ b _ _ ant   Gorgeous, showy.
4 t _ _ e _ ant   Not judging things harshly, open-minded.
5 fl _ _ _ ant   Treating serious things lightly.
6 o _ s _ r _ ant   Quick to notice things.
7 a _ a _ ant   Unyielding, very sure about something.
8 i _ c _ _ _ ant   Unceasing.
9 r _ _ e _ ant   To the point.
10 e _ o _ b _ _ ant   Excessively expensive.
11 a _ u _ _ ant   Plentiful.
12 bl _ _ ant   Very obvious.

Make NOUNS ending in `ance` or `ancy` from the ADJECTIVES below.

ADJECTIVE	NOUN	ADJECTIVE	NOUN
1 reluctant	_____	5 poignant	_____
2 tolerant	_____	6 vigilant	_____
3 buoyant	_____	7 ignorant	_____
4 redundant	_____	8 pregnant	_____

Choose `ant` or `ent` to complete the ADJECTIVES below.

1 const_____	5 viol_____	9 anci_____
2 subsequ_____	6 hesit_____	10 signific_____
3 milit_____	7 transpar_____	11 innoc_____
4 indign_____	8 magnific_____	12 triumph_____

Suffix ic

The suffix ic is a common **ADJECTIVE** suffix which comes from the Greek language. It means 'like' or 'relating to'.

e.g. athletic = like an athlete

geographic = relating to Geography

Re-order the syllables below to make 10 words ending in ic.
Each word will have 4 or 5 syllables.

1 tō crat ar ic is _____

2 hol ic cō al _____

3 thū tic si as en _____

4 ō ic pan ram _____

5 mic pō hy der _____

6 tic is fā tal _____

7 dem ic crat ō _____

8 nos dī ag tic _____

9 tō gen ic phō _____

10 ic crō scop mī _____

Now use each of the above words to complete the sentences below.

1 _____ drinks always gave her a headache.

2 The doctor's _____ skills were excellent.

3 We stopped to admire the _____ view.

4 Cute babies are often more _____ than their parents!

5 He came from an old and _____ family.

6 Many organisms are _____ in size.

7 Most European countries have a _____ style of government.

8 The History teacher was very _____ about his subject.

9 He had a very _____ approach to life.

10 The nurse approached the man with a huge _____ syringe.

Choose 4 of the ic words below and use them in sentences of your own.

optimistic   dramatic   toxic   sarcastic   prehistoric

chaotic   authentic   exotic   heroic   majestic

_____

_____

_____

_____

Suffix ive

The suffix ive normally indicates an **ADJECTIVE** and is of Latin origin.
There is often a related **VERB** ending in 'ate', 'de' or 'nd'.

	NOUN	**ADJECTIVE**
e.g.	create	creative
	evade	evasive
	defend	defensive

Below are the meanings of 10 common ive words. What are they?

1   Not cheap.   e _ _ _ _ _ ive

2   Likes to chat.   t _ _ _ _ _ ive

3   Covering a wide area.   ex _ _ _ _ ive

4   Opposite of positive.   n _ _ _ _ ive

5   Nice to look at.   a _ _ _ _ _ _ ive

6   Very large.   m _ _ _ ive

7   Curious, nosy.   in _ _ _ _ _ _ ive

8   Responsive to the feelings of others.   s _ _ _ _ _ ive

9   Striking.   im _ _ _ _ _ ive

10 Gets on well with others.   co _ _ _ _ _ _ ive

The words below are slightly less common. Use each one to complete the sentences.

deceptive   distinctive   impulsive   pensive
repulsive   persuasive   selective   lucrative

1   His business was so _____ that he soon became rich.

2   Most people find snakes _____ creatures.

3   The salesman was so _____ that I ended up buying the camera.

4   The child's _____ behaviour led him to do many things without thinking what the result would be.

5   I am very _____ about what T.V. programmes I watch.

6   I could tell by the _____ look on her face that she was thinking of something sad or serious.

7   We could always recognise him by his _____ hair style.

8   The hill was _____ in that it was much steeper than it looked from a distance.

Suffix ive

Change the following VERBS into ADJECTIVES ending in ive .

1 repeat _____

2 imagine _____

3 attend _____

4 appreciate _____

5 divide _____

6 inform _____

7 progress _____

8 receive _____

9 seduce _____

10 offend _____

11 corrode _____

12 decorate _____

Solve the anagrams below to complete the sentences with words ending in ive . *(The first letter has been given to help you.)*

1 The police made _____ enquiries in their search for the missing child. (u h a v e̱ s i x t e)

2 The dog was carrying an _____ amount of body fat because its owner overfed it. (s x v c s e̱ e i e)

3 A _____ person does not like to share things. (i o s s p̱ v e e s s)

4 Parents who are _____ allow their children a lot of freedom. (e s i v e m p̱ i r s)

5 Acid is a _____ substance, and must be handled with care. (v r s c̱ i o o r e)

6 The evidence was not _____ enough to convict the man of the crime. (v s n u c̱ l e o c i)

7 A _____ habit is one which you can't stop doing, such as smoking. (i c̱ m p s u v o e l)

8 The boy looked very _____ when he was being told off, but normally he was very defiant. (v m e u i s̱ b s i s)

9 The bombing raids continued for seven _____ nights. (v c n e i c̱ u e o s t)

10 The girl was suspended for her _____ (s a̱ i r s g e e g v) and _____ (r i i s t e ḏ u v p) behaviour.

Suffix ate

The suffix ate is normally a <u>VERB</u> ending, but in some words it denotes an <u>ADJECTIVE</u>. When ate is a <u>VERB</u> ending, it is pronounced with a long /ā/ sound because of the stress. e.g. creáte

But when it is an <u>ADJECTIVE</u> ending, it is pronounced like 'ut' because it is unstressed. e.g. prívate

Some words with ate suffix can function as a <u>VERB</u> or a <u>NOUN</u> depending on how they are pronounced.

e.g.   separáte = VERB   He tried to separáte the wires.
        séparate = ADJ   They lived in séparate houses.

<u>Put the syllables in order to make 10 ADJECTIVES ending in ate.</u>
<u>Then match each one to the correct meanings as in the example.</u>

a) cū rate ac   _____accurate_____   Unable to read or write.

b) ate prō ap pri   _____   Random, not discerning.

c) pas ate com sion   _____   Suitable.

d) lit er il ate   _____   Able to express oneself well.

e) stin ob ate   _____   On purpose.

f) tim ate ul   _____   Showing pity.

g) late ar ū tic   _____   Exact.

h) lib ate dē er   _____   Stubborn.

i) rate o ē lab   _____   Final.

j) ate dis in in crim   _____   Worked out in detail, ornate.

<u>Use the ate ADJECTIVES below in sentences of your own.</u>

affectionate   delicate   considerate   fortunate   immediate

_____
_____
_____
_____
_____
_____
_____

Suffix ary

The suffix ary usually denotes an **ADJECTIVE**, although some words ending in ary are **NOUNS**. It means 'belonging to' and originates from Latin.

e.g. imaginary = belonging to the imagination.

QUIZ: Check the meaning of any ary words you don't know to answer the questions below.

1   If you have a <u>sedentary</u> job, are you likely to work in an office or outside?

2   If the police make <u>preliminary</u> enquiries, would it be at the beginning or end of their investigation?

3   If you went to an exhibition of <u>contemporary</u> Art, would the pictures be modern or from long ago?

4   What part of the body would be affected if you had <u>pulmonary</u> disease?

5   What would you do if you spotted an <u>incendiary</u> device?

6   Would a child be rewarded or punished for <u>exemplary</u> behaviour?

7   If you buy a <u>concessionary</u> ticket, would you pay more or less than the normal fare?

8   If somebody makes a <u>complimentary</u> remark about you, would you be pleased or insulted?

9   If somebody does something for <u>mercenary</u> reasons, does he/she wish to help people or make money?

10   Can Robin Hood be described as a <u>luminary</u> hero or a <u>legendary</u> hero?

Write your own sentences for the ary words below.
Make sure you learn the spellings.

temporary   necessary   stationary   voluntary   solitary

_____

_____

_____

_____

_____

_____

Suffix ory

> The suffix ory originates from Latin and means 'belonging to' or 'relating to'. It has the same pronunciation as ary. Most words ending in ory are <u>ADJECTIVES</u>.   e.g. circulat<u>ory</u> = relating to circulation.
> but some are <u>NOUNS:</u>   e.g. direct<u>ory</u>

<u>Complete the sentences below which all contain words ending in</u> ory.

1   If something is compuls<u>ory</u> or obligat<u>ory</u>, you _____

_____

2   If you get a satisfact<u>ory</u> school report, it _____

_____

3   A predat<u>ory</u> animal is one which _____

_____

4   If you are working in an advis<u>ory</u> role, you _____

_____

5   If you make a contradict<u>ory</u> remark, you _____

_____

6   If you make an inflammat<u>ory</u> speech, you _____

_____

7   If you have respit<u>ory</u> problems, you _____

_____

8   If you have an explorat<u>ory</u> operation, the purpose is _____

_____

9   If you make a derogat<u>ory</u> remark about something, you _____

_____

10   If something is transit<u>ory</u>, it _____

_____

<u>Choose</u> ary <u>or</u> ory <u>to complete the words below which are all NOUNS.</u>

1 bound_____	7 diction_____	13 vocabul_____
2 categ_____	8 dormit_____	14 lavat_____
3 centen_____	9 itiner_____	15 sanctu_____
4 laborat_____	10 refect_____	16 direct_____
5 territ_____	11 obitu_____	17 burgl_____
6 annivers_____	12 conservat_____	18 secret_____

Adjective Practice Sheet

Apply your suffixing rules to do the word-sums below. You will have to DOUBLE, DROP 'e', CHANGE 'y' to 'i' or JUST ADD.

1 glory + ous = _____
2 red + ish = _____
3 horrify + ing = _____
4 defect + ive = _____
5 smoke + less = _____
6 spike + y = _____
7 need + y = _____
8 brute + al = _____

9 mercy + ful = _____
10 lone + some = _____
11 cure + able = _____
12 blame + worthy = _____
13 grub + y = _____
14 terrify + ed = _____
15 globe + al = _____
16 artist + ic = _____

Choose **y**, **ish** or **some** to complete the words below.

1 sponge + _____ = _____
2 shrew + _____ = _____
3 loath + _____ = _____
4 feather + _____ = _____
5 white + _____ = _____

6 knot + _____ = _____
7 trouble + _____ = _____
8 thug + _____ = _____
9 weary + _____ = _____
10 grease + _____ = _____

Choose **ful** or **less** to complete the words below.

1 seed + _____ = _____
2 bounty + _____ = _____
3 penny + _____ = _____
4 regret + _____ = _____
5 cease + _____ = _____

6 sorrow + _____ = _____
7 stain + _____ = _____
8 plenty + _____ = _____
9 noise + _____ = _____
10 waste + _____ = _____

Choose **able** or **ible** to complete the words below.

1 leg_____
2 cred_____
3 compar_____
4 break_____

5 change_____
6 compat_____
7 invinc_____
8 prob_____

9 permiss_____
10 inflat_____
11 memor_____
12 respons_____

Adjective Practice Sheet

Change the NOUNS below into ADJECTIVES ending in y , al or ive .

NOUN	ADJECTIVE	NOUN	ADJECTIVE
1 culture	_____	9 biology	_____
2 laziness	_____	10 juice	_____
3 aggression	_____	11 instruction	_____
4 emotion	_____	12 rust	_____
5 addiction	_____	13 secret	_____
6 fur	_____	14 legality	_____
7 coast	_____	15 fluff	_____
8 nosiness	_____	16 sensitivity	_____

Choose ent or ant to complete the words below.

1 conveni_____   5 obedi_____   9 adam_____

2 repent_____   6 toler_____   10 confide_____

3 ignor_____   7 intellig_____   11 domin_____

4 triumph_____   8 pati_____   12 rever_____

Choose the correct ADJECTIVE suffix to complete the words below.

ish   ful   ous   able   ive   ate

1 pink_____   8 delic_____   15 imaginat_____

2 danger_____   9 taste_____   16 tickl_____

3 depend_____   10 descript_____   17 moment_____

4 defect_____   11 fever_____   18 sorrow_____

5 affection_____   12 fest_____   19 baby_____

6 event_____   13 companion_____   20 fortun_____

7 outrage_____   14 compassion_____   21 excit_____

Adjective Practice Sheet

Change the NOUNS below into ADJECTIVES ending in
| ous |, | ic | or | ent |.

NOUN	ADJECTIVE		NOUN	ADJECTIVE
1 allergy	_____		9 rebellion	_____
2 caution	_____		10 violence	_____
3 absence	_____		11 chaos	_____
4 treachery	_____		12 mischief	_____
5 fraud	_____		13 urgency	_____
6 angel	_____		14 energy	_____
7 miracle	_____		15 fame	_____
8 decency	_____		16 hero	_____

Choose | tious | or | cious | to complete the words below.

1 suspi_____	5 infec_____	9 nutri_____
2 cons_____	6 ambi_____	10 viva_____
3 scrump_____	7 fero_____	11 spa_____
4 atro_____	8 supersti_____	12 preten_____

Choose the correct ADJECTIVE suffix to complete the words below.

ant   al   ible   ic   ary   worthy

1 ined_____	8 experiment_____	15 irrevers_____
2 hesit_____	9 majest_____	16 horizont_____
3 revolution_____	10 indign_____	17 scientif_____
4 diplomat_____	11 invis_____	18 volunt_____
5 tempor_____	12 disciplin_____	19 reluct_____
6 critic_____	13 neurot_____	20 provision_____
7 praise_____	14 news_____	21 pathet_____

Suffix ly as VERB Modifier

> The suffix ly denotes an **ADVERB**. Words ending in suffix ly are used as **MODIFIERS**, which means they tell us more about other words. **ADVERBS** can modify both **VERBS** and **ADJECTIVES**.
>
> **VERB**
> e.g. She spoke softly. ('Softly' tells us <u>how</u> she spoke.)
> **ADJECTIVE**
> She was extremely beautiful. ('Extremely' tells us <u>how</u> beautiful she was.)
>
> As **ADVERBS** give us additional information, you can make your writing more interesting by using them.

Add descriptive detail to the sentences below by choosing suitable ADVERBS to modify the VERBS.

1 The wind was howling _____ and the rain lashed down _____ as the campers struggled _____ to put up their tents.

2 The soft sound of piano music drifted _____ through the window as Beth paced _____ up and down the room.

3 A fly buzzed _____ as Rajinder tried _____ to concentrate on his essay.

4 Thunder rumbled _____ in the distance as the soldiers marched _____ to the front line.

5 With eyes flashing _____ and tail whipping _____ from side to side, the monster reared up on its hind legs.

6 As the children slept _____ in their beds, the snow fell _____ and _____ throughout the night.

Now choose ONE of the scenes below and write and a short, descriptive paragraph using 4 ADVERBS to make your description more interesting.

a) On the beach. b) School playground. c) City centre.

_____

_____

_____

_____

_____

_____

_____

_____

_____

Suffix |ly| as ADJECTIVE Modifier

> ## The suffix |ly| can modify **ADJECTIVES** as well as **VERBS**.
>
> **ADJECTIVE**
> e.g.   The moat was surprising<u>ly</u>   deep.
>   The shower was wonderful<u>ly</u> refreshing.
>
> ### Spelling Rule
> **If the base word ends in 'y', <u>CHANGE</u> the 'y' to 'i' when adding the suffix.**
> e.g.   eas<u>y</u> + ly = eas<u>i</u>ly
>
> **If the base word ends in 'ble', <u>CHANGE</u> to 'bly'.**
> e.g.   possi<u>ble</u> ⟶ possi<u>bly</u>
>
> **<u>JUST ADD</u> the suffix in all other cases.**

Add |ly| to the ADJECTIVES below.

1 absolute   + ly = _____
2 scruffy   + ly = _____
3 unspeakable + ly = _____
4 critical   + ly = _____
5 horrible   + ly = _____
6 sincere   + ly = _____

7 dreadful   + ly = _____
8 deceptive + ly = _____
9 intensive + ly = _____
10 extreme   + ly = _____
11 repeated + ly = _____
12 visible   + ly = _____

Use a suitable ADVERB ending in |ly| to complete the sentences below.

1   The man was _____ injured in the road accident.

2   I expected the test to be hard, but it was _____ easy.

3   The girl was _____ sorry for hurting her parents.

4   The witness described the man as being _____ dressed.

5   She was _____ sure that she had seen a U.F.O.

6   The child was _____ badly behaved.

7   The nurses in the children's ward were _____ kind.

8   I enjoyed all the circus acts, but the clowns were _____ entertaining.

9   Athletes perform feats which would be _____ difficult for most people.

10 His sprained ankle was _____ painful for a few days.

Word Formation: Practice Sheet 1

Complete each column with the appropriate NOUN, VERB or ADJECTIVE form which is related to the given word.

	NOUN	VERB	ADJECTIVE
1	education		
2		orchestrate	
3	deafness		
4	significance		
5	falsehood		
6			final
7	destruction		
8		permit	
9		terrify	
10			satisfactory
11		annoy	
12	legality		
13	creativity		
14	drama		
15		impress	
16	strength		
17		organise	
18	glory		
19	width		
20		coincide	

Word Formation: Practice Sheet 2

Complete each column with the appropriate NOUN, VERB or ADJECTIVE form which is related to the given word.

	NOUN	VERB	ADJECTIVE
1			tolerant
2		typify	
3		civilise	
4	threat		
5			supervisory
6		prosper	
7			fertile
8			successful
9	sympathy		
10	repression		
11	activity		
12		persist	
13		forget	
14	scandal		
15			moist
16		amuse	
17		horrify	
18	disobedience		
19			advisory
20		continue	

Word Formation: Practice Sheet 3

Complete each column with the appropriate NOUN, VERB or ADJECTIVE form which is related to the given word.

	NOUN	VERB	ADJECTIVE
1		imagine	
2	division		
3		beautify	
4	length		
5		develop	
6		enjoy	
7			defensive
8		criticise	
9		waste	
10			free
11	purity		
12		appreciate	
13			digestible
14			explanatory
15		glamorise	
16	obstruction		
17		deepen	
18	simplicity		
19			occupational
20		popularise	

Word Formation: Practice Sheet 4

Complete each column with the appropriate NOUN, VERB or ADJECTIVE form which is related to the given word.

	NOUN	VERB	ADJECTIVE
1		depend	
2			agreeable
3	belief		
4		publicise	
5	variation		
6		necessitate	
7			disappointed
8		complete	
9	extension		
10		break	
11	memory		
12		intensify	
13	symbol		
14		decide	
15	meaning		
16		deceive	
17			bright
18			thick
19	possession		
20		sulk	

Word Formation: Practice Sheet 5

Complete each column with the appropriate NOUN, VERB or ADJECTIVE form which is related to the given word.

	NOUN	VERB	ADJECTIVE
1	attraction		
2			hard
3		rely	
4		interfere	
5	economy		
6		compare	
7			weak
8		suspect	
9	admiration		
10		expect	
11		populate	
12	hypnotism		
13		resist	
14		manage	
15	notification		
16			adoptive
17	solidity		
18		explode	
19		boss	
20	apology		

SUMMARY OF
THE SUFFIXING RULES

JUST ADD

Just Add all <u>CONSONANT</u> suffixes (except when the base word ends in 'y' preceded by a consonant).

e.g.   hope + f̱ul = hopef̱ul   fit + ṉess = fitness

Just Add <u>VOWEL</u> suffixes when the base word has the following patterns:

showed   playing   feeding   filled

DOUBLE   (ONE-ONE-ONE RULE)

When adding a <u>VOWEL</u> suffix to a base word with <u>ONE</u> syllable, <u>ONE</u> short vowel and ending in only <u>ONE</u> consonant, you must <u>DOUBLE</u> the final consonant of the base word to keep the vowel short.

e.g.   rŭn + ing = rŭnning   flŏp + y = flŏppy

The double rule also applies in longer words if the last syllable of the base word is stressed and has the V̆C|V pattern.

e.g.   omít + ed = omitted   prefér + ing = preferring

DROP 'e'

When adding a <u>VOWEL</u> suffix to a base word ending in 'e', you must drop the 'e' of the base word.

e.g.   hate + ing = hating   shine + y = shiny

CHANGE 'y' to 'i'

When adding a <u>VOWEL</u> or <u>CONSONANT</u> suffix to a base word ending in a <u>CONSONANT</u> + 'y', you must <u>CHANGE</u> 'y' to 'i'.

e.g.   hurry + ed = hurried   pity + ful = pitiful

Do <u>NOT</u> change 'y' to 'i' if adding 'ing', or if there is a <u>VOWEL</u> before the 'y'.

e.g.   tidy + ing = tidying   display + ed = displayed

ANSWER SECTION

Worksheet 3

1 enjoyment	5 entered	9 childhood
2 poisonous	6 foolish	10 rudeness
3 classify	7 inspection	11 dependent
4 breakable	8 publicise	12 sharpen

NOUN suffixes:

enjoy<u>ment</u>, inspec<u>tion</u>, child<u>hood,</u> rude<u>ness</u>.

VERB suffixes:

public<u>ise</u>, enter<u>ed</u>, class<u>ify</u>, sharp<u>en</u>.

ADJECTIVE suffixes:

poisono<u>us</u>, fool<u>ish</u>, break<u>able</u>, depend<u>ent</u>.

Worksheet 5

1 jogger	tripped	muddy
2 winner	running	fitter
3 skinny	wagged	patted
4 funny	baggy	floppy
5 robber	hummed	tipped

Worksheet 6

dishevelled	enrolment
appealing	propeller
recoiled	quarrelsome
patrolling	pedalled
marvellous	fulfilled
repellent	prevailing

Worksheet 7

a) refer	d) prefer	g) recur
b) incur	e) occur	h) infer
c) inter	f) abhor	i) transfer

Sentences

1 incurred	5 interred	8 referred
2 transferred	6 inferred	9 abhorrence
3 preferred	7 occurred	
4 deterrent	recurring	

Worksheet 8

a) emit	d) remit	g) submit	j) upset
b) abet	e) omit	h) commit	k) outfit
c) transmit	f) acquit	i) permit	l) regret

Sentences

1 remitted	5 permitting	9 regretted
2 acquitted	6 transmitted	10 omitted
3 abetting	7 emitted	11 upsetting
4 outfitter	8 committed	12 submitted

Worksheet 9a

1 commítted	5 devéloping	9 bénefited
2 preférred	6 begínning	10 admítted
3 equípped	7 regrétted	11 recúrring
4 dífferent	8 préference	12 inhábited

Sentences

1 committed	4 equipped	7 recurring
2 beginning	5 admitted	
3 regretted	6 preferred	

Worksheet 9b

1 beginning	8 rebelled	15 marvellous
2 permitting	9 redeemed	16 enrolment
3 suffering	10 appealing	17 regretted
4 restrained	11 referred	18 profited
5 acquittal	12 admitted	19 upsetting
6 forgotten	13 plummeted	20 modelling
7 repeated	14 equipment	

Worksheet 10

1 flaming	8 lifeless	15 peaceful
2 excitement	9 grateful	16 shiny
3 hopeless	10 precisely	17 extremely
4 hazy	11 dozing	18 careful
5 icy	12 timeless	19 refusing
6 escaping	13 lazy	20 hiding
7 rudeness	14 trader	

Worksheet 11

1 management	8 bereavement	15 required
2 struggling	9 comradeship	16 completely
3 extremely	10 excitement	17 survivor
4 continuous	11 spiky	18 boredom
5 staring	12 rudeness	19 surprising
6 icy	13 inhaling	20 wheezing
7 sincerely	14 tasted	

Sentences

1 survivors, required	4 staring, spiky
2 surprising, continuous	5 struggling, icy
3 inhaling, wheezing	

Worksheet 12 Sentences

1 enforceable	5 marriageable
2 outrageous	6 knowledgeable
3 serviceable	7 advantageous
4 (un)pronounceable	8 irreplaceable

Worksheet 13a

List A words have a vowel before the 'y', whereas List B words have a consonant before the 'y'.

For List A words, Just Add suffix 's'. For List B words, change 'y' to 'i' and add suffix 'es'.

Worksheet 13b

```
a c o m e d y t v s t
j e r s e y d r a e r
e n q u i r y a r n o
s t b p u p p y m t l
s u p a r t y g y r l
a r o s c o u n t y e
y y n t o y d u t y y
g u y r n y l a d y b
p l a y v a l l e y o
r u b y o m o n k e y
a b b e y k i d n e y
```

abbey	lady	abbeys	ladies
army	monkey	armies	monkeys
boy	party	boys	parties
century	pastry	centuries	pastries
comedy	play	comedies	plays
county	pony	counties	ponies
convoy	puppy	convoys	puppies
duty	ruby	duties	rubies
essay	sentry	essays	sentries
enquiry	toy	enquiries	toys
guy	tray	guys	trays
jersey	trolley	jerseys	trolleys
kidney	valley	kidneys	valleys

Worksheet 14

1 sprays	11 repaying	21 journeyed
2 defied	12 dustiest	22 laziness
3 replying	13 dutiful	23 wearisome
4 dismayed	14 reliable	24 melodious
5 portrayed	15 copying	25 betrayal
6 deployment	16 hurried	26 industrial
7 surveyor	17 strayed	27 glorious
8 buyer	18 employing	28 merriment
9 parties	19 fanciful	29 burying
10 magnified	20 levied	30 enviable

Worksheet 15

Exercise 1

1 regretfully	4 fattening	7 prudishness
2 creamier	5 surprisingly	8 convincingly
3 funnily	6 timelessness	

Exercise 2

1 drunkenness	5 hurriedly
2 sleeplessness	6 deafening deafened
3 greediness/greediest	7 foolishness foolishly
4 wealthiest	8 gracefully

RULE PRACTICE SHEETS

Worksheet 16	Worksheet 17	Worksheet 18
healthier	operating	annoying
shunned	ageless	deleting
Danish	trimmed	grainy
grumbling	copied	spinning
journeyed	inhaling	clumsiness
knotty	bodiless	craggy
lorries	chatty	busiest
nervy	arrayed	vetted
cheerful	ticklish	roguish
trotting	tastiest	multiplied
heaviness	throbbing	bubbly
coolest	pastries	flabby
flatten	wettish	foaming
amazement	weepy	surprising
sagging	judging	stepping
fancied	thudded	windier
wheezing	refinement	hasten
awaken	tasty	plentiful
dutiful	meaner	portrayed
roomy	ugliness	extremely

Worksheet 19	Worksheet 20	Worksheet 21
friendliest	deplorable	testified
fretting	approval	occurred
noticeable	preferred	livelihood
postponing	arguing	sleeplessness
dreariness	tastier	persevering
guiltily	squatter	gossiping
whipped	advertisement	comradeship
sincerity	upsetting	confusingly
controlled	bitty	enforceable
examining	glorious	expelled
orbited	pitifully	celebrities
surveyor	receiving	lazily
grudgingly	editor	crumbly
conspiracies	signalled	courageous
excitable	starry	severity
mystifying	drunkenness	equipped
noisiest	industrial	justified
choppy	funnily	galloping
bleeding	wrinkly	defiance
emitted	wearisome	completing

Worksheet 23

1 coarseness	6	calmness
2 dryness	7	openness
3 clumsiness	8	gentleness
4 idleness	9	easiness
5 drunkenness	10	tidiness

Word Quiz

1 loneliness	6	politeness
2 dizziness	7	stillness
3 homesickness	8	shortsightedness
4 forgetfulness	9	weightlessness
5 helplessness	10	consciousness

Worksheet 24

Anagrams

1 question	5 potion	9 lotion
2 auction	6 motion	10 ration
3 fiction	7 notion	
4 diction	8 fraction	

Sentences

1 eruption	5 election	9 infections
2 reflection	6 collection	10 condition
3 starvation	7 inspection	11 attention
4 intention	8 ambition	12 vacation
		vocation

Worksheet 25

Sentences

1 concentration	5 hesitation	9 celebration
2 Revolution	6 destination	10 applications
3 operation	7 vaccination	11 decorations
4 populations	8 indication	12 explanation

Jumbled syllable exercise

1 examination	7 exasperation
2 civilisation	8 documentation
3 assassination	9 investigation
4 accommodation	10 organisation
5 communication	11 preoccupation
6 disembarcation	12 determination

The syllable before 'tion' is always stressed in these words.

Worksheet 26

NOUNS from VERBS

alteration	application
creation	confirmation
donation	qualification
instruction	opposition
introduction	observation
rotation	production
attention	restoration
hesitation	revolution
contemplation	imitation
inscription	destruction

VERBS from NOUNS

exhibit	relax
recognise	execute
devote	describe
restore	reduce
purify	communicate
interrogate	assassinate
deprive	examine
inflate	reveal
ignite	oblige
receive	prescribe

Worksheet 27

sh'n:	discussion	mansion	impression
	pension	confession	procession
zh'n:	erosion	conclusion	decision
	confusion	occasion	collision

Sentences

1 occasion	6 decisions
2 pension	7 procession
3 confession	8 discussion
	conclusion
4 impression mansion	9 confusion
5 collision	10 erosion

Worksheet 28

NOUNS from VERBS

1 comprehension	6 remission
2 explosion	7 suspension
3 commission	8 omission
4 expansion	9 persuasion
5 invasion	10 permission

Sentences

1 explosion	6 invasion
2 suspension	7 expansion
3 commission	8 omission
4 remission	9 persuasion
5 comprehension	10 permission

Worksheet 29

a	s	e	c	u	r	e	f	v	o
f	i	a	c	t	i	v	e	i	s
p	m	b	v	a	i	n	s	s	t
o	p	l	c	h	v	k	t	i	u
s	l	e	q	u	a	l	i	b	p
s	e	n	o	b	l	e	v	l	i
i	j	o	l	l	y	q	e	e	d
b	m	a	t	u	r	e	b	r	d
l	e	c	u	r	i	o	u	s	u
e	g	e	n	e	r	o	u	s	z

1 able	6 generous	11 secure
2 active	7 jolly	12 simple
3 curious	8 mature	13 stupid
4 equal	9 noble	14 vain
5 festive	10 possible	15 visible

Worksheet 29 continued

ADJECTIVES which drop 'e' when adding 'ity':
active   festive   mature   secure

ADJECTIVES which Just Add when adding 'ity':
equal   stupid

An ADJECTIVE which changes 'y' to 'i' when adding 'ity': jolly

ADJECTIVES ending in 'ble':
Change these letters to 'bility' when adding 'ity'.

Worksheet 30

Sentences
1 necessity	5 authority	9 locality
2 punctuality	6 curiosity	10 probability
3 opportunity	7 identity	
4 personality	8 captivity	

NOUNS from VERBS
1 diversity	7 futility	13 regularity
2 simplicity	8 fertility	14 flexibility
3 dignity	9 insanity	15 obscurity
4 prosperity	10 normality	16 atrocity
5 complexity	11 pomposity	
6 reality	12 severity	

Worksheet 31

1 imprisonment	6 elopement
2 compliment	7 bewilderment
3 achievement	8 requirement
accomplishment	9 astonishment
4 environment	10 fulfilment
5 nourishment	

Word search grid:

a	g	r	e	e	k	s	h	i	p
r	e	p	u	n	i	s	h	q	o
r	m	a	d	e	p	a	r	t	d
a	p	y	f	i	t	m	o	v	e
n	l	g	j	e	q	u	i	p	v
g	o	v	e	r	n	s	e	t	e
e	y	s	t	a	t	e	n	r	l
j	u	d	g	e	o	d	d	e	o
c	m	a	n	a	g	e	o	a	p
r	e	f	r	e	s	h	w	t	y

1 agree	6 employ	11 judge	16 punish
2 amuse	7 endow	12 manage	17 refresh
3 arrange	8 equip	13 move	18 ship
4 depart	9 fit	14 odd	19 state
5 develop	10 govern	15 pay	20 treat

Worksheet 32

Prefixes
1 misgovernment	12 reinforcement
2 disarmament	13 excitement
3 imprisonment	14 misalignment
4 redevelopment	15 engagement
underdevelopment	16 compartment
5 detachment	department
6 contentment	17 commitment
7 concealment	18 postponement
8 understatement	19 encampment
misstatement	20 encouragement
9 investment	21 maltreatment
10 maladjustment	22 impeachment
11 employment	23 impairment
deployment	24 complement

QUIZ
1 impairment	5 postponement
2 investment	6 complement
3 concealment	7 malgovernment
4 disarmament	8 understatement

Worksheet 33

1 competence	4 turbulence	7 deterrence
2 impudence	5 affluence	8 persistence
3 consequence	6 subsidence	

Worksheet 34

Word-meanings
a) reluctance	f) nuisance
b) resemblance	g) endurance
c) significance	h) fragrance
d) ignorance	i) grievance
e) circumstance	j) arrogance

1 assistance	11 avoidance
2 perseverance	12 coincidence
3 occurrence	13 reluctance
4 experience	14 acceptance
5 reassurance	15 residence
6 elegance	16 resistance
7 extravagance	17 insistence
8 convenience	18 audience
9 obedience	19 negligence
10 dependence	20 maintenance

Worksheet 35

1 pregnancy	5 bankruptcy	9 conspiracy
2 currency	6 infancy	secrecy
3 redundancy	7 literacy	
4 deficiency	8 emergency	

NOUNS from ADJECTIVES
1 dependency	5 leniency	9 vacancy
2 recency	6 aristocracy	10 supremacy
3 privacy	7 delicacy	11 frequency
4 fluency	8 decency	12 diplomacy

111

Worksheet 36

1 They can speak more than one language.
2 Communism.
3 Thailand, Tibet, Burma, Sri Lanka.
4 Planted a bomb, hijacked an aircraft etc. for political gain.
5 If they are discriminated against because of their age when applying for a job.
6 Out-of-date.
7 Art.
8 teetotalism.
9 positive.
10 dislike them.
11 pessimism.
12 war.
13 Jewish people.
14 unpopular.
15 a love of one's country.

Worksheet 37

1 orphanage
2 sabotage
3 beverage
4 vicarage
5 shortage
6 mortgage
7 espionage
8 package
9 percentage
10 disadvantage
11 wreckage
12 marriage
13 courage
14 plumage
15 pilgrimage

Worksheet 38

caricature	fixture	sculpture
culture	fracture	structure
erasure	future	texture
exposure	moisture	
feature	rupture	

Missing Vowel Exercise

1 miniature
2 expenditure
3 temperature
4 signature
5 furniture
6 architecture
7 literature
8 manufacture
9 leisure
10 seizure

Sentences

1 multitude
2 solitude
3 aptitude
4 fortitude

Worksheet 39

1 baby<u>hood</u>
2 workman<u>ship</u>
3 leader<u>ship</u>
4 likeli<u>hood</u>
5 nation<u>hood</u>
6 salesman<u>ship</u>
7 librarian<u>ship</u>
8 neighbour<u>hood</u>
9 sponsor<u>ship</u>
10 apprentice<u>ship</u>
11 censor<u>ship</u>
12 mother<u>hood</u>
13 woman<u>hood</u>
14 partner<u>ship</u>
15 champion<u>ship</u>
16 relation<u>ship</u>
17 hard<u>ship</u>
18 liveli<u>hood</u>
19 saint<u>hood</u>
20 scholar<u>ship</u>
21 priest<u>hood</u>

Anagrams

1 stardom
2 wisdom
3 kingdom
4 martyrdom
5 freedom
6 officialdom

Worksheet 40

Anagrams

1 climber
2 gambler
3 reporter
4 warder
5 jailer
6 smuggler
7 wrestler
8 keeper
9 speaker
10 juggler
11 painter
12 skater

Suffixing

1 sinner
2 day-tripper
3 observer
4 toddler
5 trainer
6 distiller
7 buyer
8 outfitter
9 carrier
10 retailer

Name the word

1 squatter
2 lecturer
3 globe-trotter
4 bouncer
5 commuter
6 potter
7 pensioner
8 forger
9 presenter
10 publisher

Worksheet 41

1 debtor
2 operator
3 traitor
4 proprietor
5 translator
6 ancestor
7 benefactor
8 aviator
9 competitor
10 decorator
11 conductor
12 solicitor
13 spectator
14 visitor
15 dictator

Worksheet 42

Health Practitioner
chiropodist
pharmacist
cardiologist
dentist
psychiatrist
radiologist
anaesthetist

Musician
cellist
trombonist
harpist
vocalist
flautist
pianist
violinist

Subject Specialist
sociologist
psychologist
geologist
physicist
zoologist
biologist
botanist

Job
receptionist
telephonist
florist
novelist
typist
journalist
tobacconist

Quiz
1 b)	3 a)	5 c)
2 a)	4 c)	6 a)

Worksheet 43

Nationalities
1 Arabian
2 Norwegian
3 Austrian
4 Venezuelan
5 Belgian
6 Rumanian
  Romanian
  Roumanian
7 Canadian
8 Syrian
9 Iranian
10 Tibetan
11 Korean
12 Peruvian

Words ending in 'cian'
1 optician
2 dietician
3 physician
4 mathematician
5 politician
6 technician
7 electrician
8 beautician

Anagrams
1 snowman
2 policeman
3 watchman
4 spokesman
5 foreman
6 nobleman
7 fireman
8 salesman
9 chairman
10 statesman

Worksheet 44

'ess' words
1 hostess
2 goddess
3 manageress
4 murderess
5 heiress
6 tigress
7 proprietress
8 duchess
9 mayoress
10 headmistress
11 empress
12 conductress

'ling' or 'ee'
1 earthling
2 gosling
3 addressee
4 payee
5 refugee
6 trustee
7 fledgling
8 weakling
9 divorcee
10 employee
11 detainee
12 seedling
13 amputee
14 escapee
15 sibling

Worksheet 45

1 entitlement
2 storage
3 jollity
4 heroism
5 excellence
6 preference
7 sinfulness
8 employment
9 likelihood
10 reliance
11 weariness
12 stoppage
13 sanity
14 escapism
15 annoyance
16 merriment

1 inscription
2 renovation
3 exclusion
4 adoption
5 mansion
6 intention
7 promotion
8 comprehension
9 extension
10 disruption
11 suspension
12 excursion

1 activity
2 loneliness
3 stupidity
4 cheerfulness
5 silliness
6 publicity
7 humidity
8 captivity
9 sincerity
10 nudity

1 existence
2 reluctance
3 ignorance
4 confidence
5 magnificence
6 coincidence
7 inheritance
8 innocence
9 performance
10 resemblance
11 repentance
12 insistence

Worksheet 46

1 seepage
2 defiance
3 deterrent
4 reference
5 humanity
6 slippage
7 subsidence
8 symbolism
9 betrayal
10 livelihood
11 refinement
12 ugliness
13 admittance
14 enjoyment
15 enclosure
16 boredom

1 foreigner
2 photographer
3 narrator
4 prisoner
5 inspector
6 solicitor
7 employer
8 retailer
9 sculptor
10 mayor
11 presenter
12 proprietor

1 musician
2 trustee
3 referee
4 operator
5 botanist
6 priesthood
7 receptionist
8 historian
9 Iranian
10 manageress
11 violinist
12 designer
13 hostess
14 finalist
15 sailor
16 creditor
17 comedian
18 absentee
19 director
20 entertainer
21 juror

Worksheet 47

1 commitment
2 enforcement
3 punctuality
4 exposure
5 racism
6 falsehood
7 plainness
8 merriment
9 grievance
10 conveyance
11 concealment
12 immensity
13 kinship
14 wastage
15 prettiness
16 acquittal

1 ownership
2 heroism
3 emptiness
4 priesthood
5 settlement
6 humidity
7 criticism
8 motherhood
9 formality
10 nervousness
11 barrenness
12 improvement
13 punishment
14 tourism
15 partnership
16 widowhood
17 resentment
18 bitterness
19 severity
20 mobility

Worksheet 48

1 walked   reached
2 boils
3 howling   lashing   attempted
4 gets likes
5 trying
6 gives
7 waited
8 going
9 likes

Questions

1 's' and 'ing'
2 'ed' No - many common verbs are irregular and have their own past tense form.
3 's'
4 Sentences 2 and 6. The Simple Present tense is used for general statements.
5 Sentences 4 and 9. The normal function is to describe habits or routines. It is often used with words like 'often', 'always', 'usually', etc.
6 'ing'   7 'ed'   8 'ing'

Worksheet 49

1 deafen
2 sadden(ed)
3 stiffen
4 sharpen
5 fasten
6 threaten(ed)
7 freshen
8 broaden
9 straighten
10 strengthen(ed)

Past Participle Exercise

broken	chair	stolen	car
fallen	tree	swollen	ankle
frozen	lake	woven	cloth
rotten	apple	molten	lava
shaven	head	sunken	ship

Worksheet 50

Anagrams

1 create
2 locate
3 cremate
4 narrate
5 debate
6 rotate
7 equate
8 donate
9 stagnate
10 vibrate

Sentences

1 celebrate
2 hibernate
3 imitate
4 circulates
5 demonstrate
6 estimate
7 navigate
8 emigrate
9 educate
10 decorate

Worksheet 51

1 evacuate
2 assassinated
3 devastated
4 commemorate
5 accommodate
6 congratulate
7 exaggerate
8 participate
9 accumulate
10 alleviate
11 investigate
    interrogate

Jumbled Syllables

a) circumnavigate = To sail around the world.
b) disorientate = To make somebody confused about direction.

Worksheet 51 continued

c) procrastinate = To put off doing something.
d) intoxicate = To make drunk.
e) obliterate = To wipe out.
f) contaminate = To make impure, poison with chemicals.
g) underestimate = To guess a number that is too low.
h) impersonate = To pretend to be somebody else.

Worksheet 52

1 simplify
2 clarify
3 unify
4 terrify
5 deify
6 purify
7 fortify
8 magnify
9 sanctify
10 modify

Anagrams

1 testify
2 specify
3 classify
4 pacify
5 verify
6 rectify

Sentences

1 rectify
2 classify
3 verify
4 testify
5 pacify
6 specify

Worksheet 53

1 recognise
2 terrorise
3 vandalise
4 memorise
5 emphasise
6 modernise
7 supervise
8 publicise
9 legalise
10 hypnotise
11 sympathise
12 criticise

Worksheet 54

1 jeopardise
2 ostracise
3 compromise
4 monopolise
5 synchronise
6 immobilise
7 tyrannise
8 scrutinise
9 galvanise
10 idolise

Sentences

1 scrutinised
2 synchronised
3 tyrannised
4 ostracise
5 jeopardised
6 monopolise
7 galvanised
8 immobilise
9 idolised
10 compromise

Worksheet 55

1 finalise
2 expelled
3 captivate
4 denied
5 referring
6 idealise
7 moisturise
8 concealed
9 hurrying
10 simplified
11 instilled
12 privatise
13 legalise
14 carried
15 typify
16 vaccinated

1 signify
2 familiarise
3 locate
4 navigate
5 sterilise
6 generate
7 classify
8 pollinate
9 vacate
10 itemise
11 fossilise
12 terrify
13 intoxicate
14 victimise
15 brutalise
16 fortify
17 qualify
18 illuminate

114

Worksheet 55 continued

1 naturalise	7 activate	13 equalise
2 solidify	8 mobilise	14 fertilise
3 purify	9 publicise	15 glorify
4 modernise	10 falsify	16 originate
5 intensify	11 co-operate	
6 domesticate	12 scandalise	

Worksheet 56a

(Suggested answers only – other answers are possible for some sentences.)

'ing' Adjectives	'ed' Adjectives
1 crying, weeping, screaming	1 boiled, bottled
2 speeding	2 painted, decorated
3 freezing	3 baked
4 burning	4 endangered
5 charging	5 withered
6 flying	6 abandoned
7 cheering	7 retired
8 dying	8 baked, boiled, fried, etc. scrambled, fried, poached, etc.

Worksheet 56b

Anagrams

1 excited	5 frustrated
2 disgusted	6 worried
3 amazed	7 thrilled
4 annoyed	8 embarrassed

Sentences *(suggestions only)*

1 frightening	5 humiliating embarrassing
2 interesting, fascinating	
3 confusing	6 terrifying, horrifying frightening
4 amusing, exciting	

Worksheet 57 *(suggested answers only)*

1 smelly, woolly, fluffy.
2 sunny, rainy, showery, windy, breezy, foggy, snowy, stormy, thundery.
3 (as for No. 2).
4 juicy, tangy, tasty.
5 rusty, shiny, classy, dirty.
6 tasty, spicy, salty, fatty.
7 fluffy, furry, cuddly.
8 witty, funny.
9 sandy, rocky, stony, pebbly.
10 frizzy, curly, wavy, shiny.
11 fizzy, milky, tasty.
12 muddy, dirty, shiny.

Anagrams

1 spotty	4 spiky	7 salty	10 itchy
2 rusty	5 floppy	8 chatty	11 gloomy
3 gritty	6 stony	9 slimy	12 guilty

Worksheet 58

'ful' only	'less' only	'ful' and 'less'
hate	fault	hope
play	sense	thought
watch	change	shame
dread	regard	colour
distrust	odour	mercy
fate	breath	cheer

1 defenceless	5 dutiful	9 joyless
2 spotless	6 penniless	10 fanciful
3 playful	7 tuneless	11 fruitful
4 bodiless	8 gleeful	12 revengeful

Worksheet 59

1 adventuresome	11 seaworthy
2 quarrelsome	12 wearisome
3 blameworthy	13 gruesome
4 troublesome	14 praiseworthy
5 businesslike	15 ladylike
6 lifelike	16 wholesome
7 meddlesome	17 cumbersome
8 roadworthy	18 warlike
9 handsome	19 worrisome
10 sylphlike	20 newsworthy

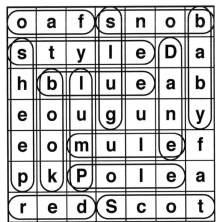

1 babyish	6 mulish	11 stylish
2 bluish	7 oafish	12 snobbish
3 bookish	8 Polish	13 sluggish
4 Danish	9 reddish	14 sheepish
5 lumpish	10 Scottish	

Worksheet 60

1 envious	6 furious	11 cautious
2 famous	7 generous	12 marvellous
3 humorous	8 curious	13 enormous
4 mischievous	9 mysterious	14 courageous
5 ravenous	10 glamorous	15 gluttonous

Sentences

1 oblivious	3 carnivorous herbivorous
2 industrious	4 monotonous

Worksheet 61

NOUNS from ADJECTIVES

1 miracle
2 consciousness
3 generosity
4 variety
5 envy
6 glamour
7 courtesy
8 religion
9 curiosity
10 prestige
11 anxiety
12 treachery

ADJECTIVES from NOUNS

1 prosperous
2 monotonous
3 furious
4 infamous
5 hilarious
6 populous
7 grievous
8 victorious
9 disastrous
10 vigorous

Quiz

1 When everybody without exception agrees.

2 Skin.   Some types of rock.
   (Other answers possible.)

3 Nonsense, because you have a high fever.

4 A lot, as a gregarious person is very sociable.

5 A lot of respect, but it might not be genuine!

6 A lot.

7 Not needed.

8 Good – a pompous person is full of self-importance.

Worksheet 62

1 conscientious
2 ostentatious
3 scrumptious nutritious
4 superstitious
5 flirtatious
6 surreptitious

1 voracious
2 avaricious
3 ferocious
4 malicious
5 vivacious

1 spacious
2 suspicious
3 infectious
4 fictitious
5 gracious
6 precious
7 pretentious
8 repetitious
9 cautious
10 vicious

Worksheet 63

ADJECTIVES derived from Latin

1 dental
2 legal
3 fiscal
4 rural
5 corporal
6 fatal
7 final
8 initial
9 maternal
10 gradual
11 annual
12 spinal
13 naval
14 vocal
15 verbal
16 manual

Sentences

1 corporal   (il)legal
2 maternal
3 manual   rural
4 vocal
5 final   verbal
6 fatal
7 spinal   initial
8 naval
9 dental

Worksheet 64

1 external
2 ideal
3 punctual
4 perpetual
5 functional
6 nasal
7 optional
8 jovial
9 occasional
10 trivial
11 filial
12 medieval
13 principal
14 universal
15 ornamental

1 optical
2 fanatical
3 sceptical
4 critical
5 comical
6 economical
7 identical
8 spherical
9 tyrannical
10 biographical
11 chronological
12 egotistical

Worksheet 65

1 beneficial
2 racial
3 financial
4 crucial
5 facial
superficial

1 torrential
2 essential
3 partial
4 potential
5 confidential

1 commercial
2 presidential
3 spatial
4 substantial
5 artificial
6 provincial
7 preferential
8 residential
9 influential
10 glacial
11 martial
12 judicial

Worksheet 66

1 approachable
2 bearable
3 desirable
4 durable
5 irritable
6 noticeable
7 affordable
8 portable
9 predictable
10 inevitable
11 irretrievable
12 inadvisable
13 insufferable
14 remarkable
15 inhospitable

Worksheet 67

1 horrible
2 possible
3 sensible
4 inedible
5 visible

1 audible
2 eligible
3 feasible
4 flexible
5 gullible
6 incredible
7 indelible
8 invincible
9 legible
10 responsible

1 charitable
2 payable
3 accessible
4 permissible
5 dependable
6 preventable
7 divisible
8 plausible
9 fashionable
10 susceptible
11 inseparable
12 excitable

Worksheet 68

1 absorbent = Like a sponge.
2 adjacent = Next to.
3 apparent = Clear to sight or mind.
4 competent = Efficient.
5 dependent = Reliant.
6 convenient = Suitable, within reach.
7 frequent = Often.
8 insolent = Rude.
9 permanent = Lasting indefinitely.
10 potent = Powerful.

Worksheet 68 continued

1 Open-ended – any situation that is upsetting or disappointing.
2 Good results.
3 No money and in debt.
4 War.
5 Spoil.
6 When they have done something that they regret and feel sorry about.
7 Very little.
8 Only a little.
9 They would stick out.
10 Respect.

Worksheet 69

1 repugnant	5 flippant	9 relevant
2 jubilant	6 observant	10 exorbitant
3 flamboyant	7 adamant	11 abundant
4 tolerant	8 incessant	12 blatant

1 reluctance	4 redundancy	7 ignorance
2 tolerance	5 poignancy	8 pregnancy
3 buoyancy	6 vigilance	

1 constant	5 violent	9 ancient
2 subsequent	6 hesitant	10 significant
3 militant	7 transparent	11 innocent
4 indignant	8 magnificent	12 triumphant

Worksheet 70

1 aristocratic	5 hypodermic	9 photogenic
2 alcoholic	6 fatalistic	10 microscopic
3 enthusiastic	7 democratic	
4 panoramic	8 diagnostic	

Sentences

1 alcoholic	5 aristocratic	9 fatalistic
2 diagnostic	6 microscopic	10 hypodermic
3 panoramic	7 democratic	
4 photogenic	8 enthusiastic	

Worksheet 71

1 expensive	5 attractive	9 impressive
2 talkative	6 massive	10 co-operative
3 extensive	7 inquisitive	
4 negative	8 sensitive	

Sentences

1 lucrative	4 impulsive	7 distinctive
2 repulsive	5 selective	8 deceptive
3 persuasive	6 pensive	

Worksheet 72

1 repetitive	5 divisive	9 seductive
2 imaginative	6 informative	10 offensive
3 attentive	7 progressive	11 corrosive
4 appreciative	8 receptive	12 decorative

Worksheet 72 continued

Anagrams

1 exhaustive	5 corrosive	9 consecutive
2 excessive	6 conclusive	10 aggressive
3 possessive	7 compulsive	disruptive
4 permissive	8 submissive	

Worksheet 73

a) accurate = Exact.
b) appropriate = Suitable.
c) compassionate = Showing pity.
d) illiterate = Unable to read or write.
e) obstinate = Stubborn.
f) ultimate = Final.
g) articulate = Able to express oneself well.
h) deliberate = On purpose.
i) elaborate = Worked out in detail.
j) indiscriminate = Random, not discerning.

Worksheet 74

1 in an office	6 rewarded
2 beginning	7 less
3 modern	8 pleased
4 lungs	9 make money
5 run away as fast as possible and dial 999!	10 legendary

Worksheet 75

1st exercise open-ended

1 boundary	7 dictionary	13 vocabulary
2 category	8 dormitory	14 lavatory
3 centenary	9 itinerary	15 sanctuary
4 laboratory	10 refectory	16 directory
5 territory	11 obituary	17 burglary
6 anniversary	12 conservatory	18 secretary

Worksheet 76

1 glorious	7 needy	13 grubby
2 reddish	8 brutal	14 terrified
3 horrifying	9 merciful	15 global
4 defective	10 lonesome	16 artistic
5 smokeless	11 curable	
6 spiky	12 blameworthy	

1 spongy	5 whitish	9 wearisome
2 shrewish	6 knotty	10 greasy
3 loathsome	7 troublesome	
4 feathery	8 thuggish	

1 seedless	5 ceaseless	9 noiseless
2 bountiful	6 sorrowful	10 wasteful
3 penniless	7 stainless	
4 regretful	8 plentiful	

1 legible	5 changeable	9 permissible
2 credible	6 compatible	10 inflatable
3 comparable	7 invincible	11 memorable
4 breakable	8 probable	12 responsible

Worksheet 77

1	cultural	9	biological
2	lazy	10	juicy
3	aggressive	11	instructive
4	emotional	12	rusty
5	addictive	13	secretive
6	furry	14	legal
7	coastal	15	fluffy
8	nosy	16	sensitive

1	conveni**ent**	7	intelli**gent**
2	repent**ant**	8	pati**ent**
3	ignor**ant**	9	adam**ant**
4	triumph**ant**	10	confid**ent**
5	obedi**ent**	11	domin**ant**
6	toler**ant**	12	rever**ent**

1	pink**ish**	12	fest**ive**
2	danger**ous**	13	companion**able**
3	depend**able**	14	compassion**ate**
4	defect**ive**	15	imaginative
5	affection**ate**	16	tickl**ish**
6	event**ful**	17	moment**ous**
7	outrage**ous**	18	sorrow**ful**
8	delic**ate**	19	baby**ish**
9	taste**ful**	20	fortun**ate**
10	descript**ive**	21	excit**able**
11	fever**ish**		

Worksheet 78

1	allergic	9	rebellious
2	cautious	10	violent
3	absent	11	chaotic
4	treacherous	12	mischievous
5	fraudulent	13	urgent
6	angelic	14	energetic
7	miraculous	15	famous
8	decent	16	heroic

1	suspi**cious**	7	fero**cious**
2	cons**cious**	8	supersti**tious**
3	scrump**tious**	9	nutri**tious**
4	atro**cious**	10	viva**cious**
5	infec**tious**	11	spa**cious**
6	ambi**tious**	12	preten**tious**

1	ined**ible**	12	disciplin**ary**
2	hesit**ant**	13	neuro**tic**
3	revolution**ary**	14	news**worthy**
4	diploma**tic**	15	irrevers**ible**
5	tempor**ary**	16	horizont**al**
6	criti**cal**	17	scientif**ic**
7	praise**worthy**	18	volunt**ary**
8	experiment**al**	19	reluct**ance**
9	majes**tic**	20	provision**al**
10	indign**ant**	21	pathe**tic**
11	invis**ible**		

Worksheet 79 *(Suggested answers only)*

1 furiously / deafeningly / demonically
mercilessly / unceasingly / relentlessly
valiantly / heroically / unsuccessfully

Worksheet 79 continued

2 melodiously / soothingly / faintly
nervously / anxiously / slowly

3 noisily / irritatingly / intrusively / persistently
desperately / unsuccessfully / hopelessly

4 ominously / faintly / disturbingly / threateningly
wearily / silently / reluctantly

5 menacingly / malevolently
furiously / viciously

6 soundly / deeply / peacefully
silently / steadily / magically / ceaselessly

Worksheet 80

1	absolutely	5	horribly	9	intensively
2	scruffily	6	sincerely	10	extremely
3	unspeakably	7	dreadfully	11	repeatedly
4	critically	8	deceptively	12	visibly

(Suggestions only)

1 fatally / critically / seriously
2 surprisingly / unexpectedly
3 deeply / sincerely / genuinely
4 smartly / scruffily / casually
5 absolutely / completely
6 extremely / impossibly / unbelievably
7 wonderfully / incredibly / extremely
8 especially / particularly
9 impossibly / extremely
10 extremely / cripplingly / dreadfully / slightly

Worksheet 81

	NOUN	VERB	ADJECTIVE
1	education	**educate**	**education**
2	**orchestra**	orchestrate	**orchestral**
3	deafness	**deafen**	**deaf(ening)**
4	significance	**signify**	**significant**
5	falsehood	**falsify**	**false**
6	**finality**	**finalise**	final
7	destruction	**destroy**	**destructive**
8	**permission**	permit	**permissive**
9	**terror**	terrify	**terrifying**
10	**satisfaction**	**satisfy**	satisfactory
11	**annoyance**	annoy	**annoying**
12	legality	**legalise**	**legal**
13	creativity	**create**	**creative**
14	drama	**dramatise**	**dramatic**
15	**impression**	impress	**impressive**
16	strength	**strengthen**	**strong**
17	**organisation**	**organise**	**organisational**
18	glory	**glorify**	**glorious**
19	width	**widen**	**wide**
20	**coincidence**	coincide	**coincidental**

Worksheet 82

	NOUN	VERB	ADJECTIVE
1	toleration	tolerate	tolerant
2	type	typify	typical
3	civilisation	civilise	civilised
4	threat	threaten	threatening
5	supervision	supervise	supervisory
6	prosperity	prosper	prosperous
7	fertility	fertilise	fertile
8	success	succeed	successful
9	sympathy	sympathise	sympathetic
10	repression	repress	repressive
11	activity	activate	active
12	persistence	persist	persistent
13	forgetfulness	forget	forgetful
14	scandal	scandalise	scandalous
15	moisture	moisten	moist
16	amusement	amuse	amusing
17	horror	horrify	horrifying
18	disobedience	disobey	disobedient
19	advice	advise	advisory
20	continuation	continue	continuous

Worksheet 83

	NOUN	VERB	ADJECTIVE
1	imagination	imagine	imaginative
2	division	divide	divisive
3	beauty	beautify	beautiful
4	length	lengthen	long
5	development	develop	developing
6	enjoyment	enjoy	enjoyable
7	defence	defend	defensive
8	criticism	criticise	critical
9	waste(fulness)	waste	wasteful
10	freedom	free	free
11	purity	purify	pure
12	appreciation	appreciate	appreciative
13	digestion	digest	digestible
14	explanation	explain	explanatory
15	glamour	glamorise	glamorous
16	obstruction	obstruct	obstructive
17	depth	deepen	deep
18	simplicity	simplify	simple
19	occupation	occupy	occupational
20	popularity	popularise	popular

Worksheet 84

	NOUN	VERB	ADJECTIVE
1	dependence	depend	dependent
2	agreement	agree	agreeable
3	belief	believe	believable
4	publicity	publicise	public
5	variation	vary	various
6	necessity	necessitate	necessary
7	disappointment	disappoint	disappointed
8	completion	complete	complete
9	extension	extend	extensive
10	breakage	break	breakable
11	memory	memorise	memorable
12	intensity	intensify	intense
13	symbol	symbolise	symbolic
14	decision	decide	decisive
15	meaning	mean	meaningful
16	deception	deceive	deceptive
17	brightness	brighten	bright
18	thickness	thicken	thick
19	possession	possess	possessive
20	sulkiness	sulk	sulky

Worksheet 85

	NOUN	VERB	ADJECTIVE
1	attraction	attract	attractive
2	hardness	harden	hard
3	reliance	rely	reliant
4	interference	interfere	interfering
5	economy	economise	economical
6	comparison	compare	comparable
7	weakness	weaken	weak
8	suspicion	suspect	suspicious
9	admiration	admire	admirable
10	expectation	expect	expectant
11	population	populate	populous
12	hypnotism	hypnotise	hypnotic
13	resistance	resist	resistant
14	management	manage	manageable
15	notification	notify	notifiable
16	adoption	adopt	adoptive
17	solidity	solidify	solid
18	explosion	explode	explosive
19	boss(iness)	boss	bossy
20	apology	apologise	apologetic